Newnes Guide to Satellite TV

Newnes Guide to Satellite TV

Installation, reception and repair

D. J. Stephenson
BA, IEng, FSERT

Heinemann Newnes

Heinemann Newnes
An imprint of Heinemann Professional Publishing Ltd
Halley Court, Jordan Hill, Oxford OX2 8EJ

OXFORD   LONDON   MELBOURNE   AUCKLAND   SINGAPORE
IBADAN NAIROBI GABORONE KINGSTON

First published 1990

British Library Cataloguing in Publication Data
Stephenson, D. J.
  Newnes guide to satellite television: installation
  reception and repair.
  1. Television equipment: Receivers. Maintenance & repair
  I. Title
  621.38887

ISBN 0 434 91818 0

Typeset, printed and bound in Great Britain by
Redwood Press Limited
Melksham, Wiltshire

Contents

Preface

Many TV/video technicians as well as aerial riggers are currently starting to dabble in this relatively new domestic market. The problem is that many TV/video technicians have trouble acquiring the skills of the aerial rigger and likewise the aerial rigger might have difficulty with the electronics side of the trade. The DIY enthusiast, on the other hand, may have little knowledge of either. It is evident that a broad-based book, such as this, can act as a foundation course for all those interested in the practical side of the subject, as well as being a handy reference source.

The treatment is pitched at a level above a simple installation guide but well below an involved theoretical textbook. As service technicians, we do not really need to know the 'ins and outs' of launching a satellite and maintaining its station keeping accuracy etc. It is sufficient, for our purposes, to treat a satellite as a microwave TV transmitter which just happens to be in the sky. The book is put together in such a way that technicians, aerial riggers or DIY enthusiasts can study the practical side of the subject to a range of different levels or interests, to suit his/her requirements at the time. Although the trade can be practised in a qualitative way, with little or no knowledge of the underlying principles, it does help if, dare I say it, a little school 'mathematics' is recalled. To understand the basic principles of satellite TV reception requires nothing more than the use of a little elementary trigonometry and algebra. However, many tables and graphs are provided so that underlying relationships can be readily visualized.

Most practical books available on the subject of satellite television are relatively expensive and mainly American in origin. Unfortunately, these contain much material not relevant to European satellite broadcasting. Europe seems to have exclusively adopted Ku-band communication. Interest in low power satellite reception has in the past received little public interest, mainly due to the size, appearance and expense of the equipment. In any case, programme providers are either switching or duplicating their offerings to the newer medium power satellites. The recent launch of the medium power Astra 1A satellite has led to antennae of an acceptable size, and low cost receiving equipment. Up to three Astra satellites are proposed, furthermore, BSB are operating a 'UK specific' high power DBS satellite, Marcopol 1. With the future launch and operation of the international medium power Eutelsat II series and the Intellsat VI series demand will grow for small motorized systems capable of tracking the entire geo-arc for medium power FSS band satellites. These systems are not likely to be the monsters we have seen in the past and it is hoped that smaller 'polar mount' dishes will be available in the not too distant future. Nevertheless, the vast majority of installations in the UK will probably be for low cost fixed satellite systems for Astra and BSB. The long term trend will probably be steered toward the 'Euro-telly', an integrated TV set with full satellite 1st IF processing. This species would incorporate C-MAC, D2MAC, DMAC; PAL and SE-CAM multi-standard compatability, leading to full, 16:9 aspect ratio, high definition TV by the end of the century. It is up to all concerned to ensure the future success of all satellite broadcasting.

Acknowledgements

The Author would like to thank the following for their help in the compilation of this book.
A. P. Stephenson (Author of waveguide section)
Derek Bellingham (Service Manager: Tatung (UK) Ltd)
Vannessa O'Connor (Eutelsat)
Tim Stephens (Technical Adviser: Hilti (Gt Britain) Limited)
C. N. Morley (Technical Sales Manager: The Rawlplug Company)
Société Européenne des Satellites (Astra)
The Independent Broadcasting Authority
Mrs B. K. Allgood (Confederation of Aerial Industries)
Trevor Pinch (Director: Morris & Pinch Ltd)
Mr R. F. Webster (Managing Director: Webro (Long Eaton) Ltd)
Volex Radex Ltd

1 Overview of satellite TV

Introduction

Direct-to-home satellite TV, although not intended as such, has been with us now for a number of years. A few enthusiasts gathered together the rudiments of a satellite receiving system and eavesdropped on the programme material destined for cable operators via low power general telecommunications satellites. Equipment, mainly from outside Europe, was imported to supply this relatively small demand. This was usually expensive, cumbersome and indescribably ugly. Reception was often poor in heavy rain or cloudy conditions, so it was not surprising that there was little public interest. Clearly, a large potential market for direct-to-home satellite TV was there if only cheaper equipment and smaller dishes were possible. This requirement was satisfied with the successful launch and operation of the semi-DBS Astra 1A satellite by a European based consortium. A new mass market was ripe for picking as low cost reception was made possible using a smallish dish of dustbin-lid-sized dimensions in conjunction with a small dedicated set-top receiver box. The giant domestic electronics manufacturers and their established dealer networks quickly stepped in to meet increased demand. With the introduction of DBS, the future looks good for all those connected with domestic electronics.

Basic terms and concepts

For those new to telecommunications, who are unfamiliar with some of the basic terms and concepts used, here follows a brief preparatory section of basic principles necessary for the understanding of satellite reception. Trained technicians may like to skip this section.

Sinusoidal electromagnetic waves (e/m waves)

All radio and television signals consist of electrical and magnetic fields which, in free space, travel at the speed of light (approximately 186 000 miles per second or 3×10^8 metres per second). These waves consist of an *electric field (E)*, measured in volts per metre and a *magnetic field (H)*, measured in amps per metre. The E and H field components are always at right angles to each other and the direction of travel is always at right angles to both fields. The amplitudes vary sinusoidally as they travel through space. In fact, it is impossible to produce a non-sinusoidal e/m wave! (The importance of this statement will be grasped more easily when modulation is discussed.)

The sinewave (see Figure 1.1)

Cycle: One complete electrical sequence.
Peak value (V_p): Maximum positive or negative value – also called the amplitude.
Period (t): Time to complete one cycle.
Frequency (f): Number of cycles per second measured in Hertz (Hz). (One Hertz = one cycle per second). It follows that period and frequency are reciprocals of each other:

$t = 1/f$

Commonly used multiples of the Hertz are:

Kilohertz (kHz) $= 10^3$ Hz $= 1000$ Hz
Megahertz (MHz) $= 10^6$ Hz $= 1\,000\,000$ Hz
Gigahertz (GHz) $= 10^9$ Hz $= 1\,000\,000\,000$ Hz

RMS value: This is 0.707 of the peak value and, unless otherwise stated, any reference to voltage or current in technical literature is normally taken to mean this value. For example, the supply mains in the UK is a sinusoidal variation, stated to be '240 volts' so the peak value is $240/0.707 = 339$ volts.

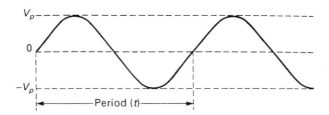

Figure 1.1 *The sinewave*

Angular velocity (ω)

This is an indirect way of expressing the frequency:

$\omega = 2\pi f$ radians per second.

Instead of considering the number of complete cycles, angular velocity is a measure of how fast the vector angle is changing. The voltage equation of a sine wave, which gives the instantaneous value (*v*) of a sine wave at any point in the cycle is given by:

$$v = V_p \sin \theta$$

where V_p is the peak voltage and θ is an angle measured in radians (not degrees). There are 2π radians in a circle and, since the sine wave can be visualized as a vector rotating in a circle, the above equation can be written in terms of frequency and angle

$$v = V_p \sin 2\pi ft$$

For convenience and brevity, the $2\pi f$ part is often lumped together and given the title of angular velocity (ω). Using this notation, the equation of the sine wave can be written as:

$$v = V_p \sin \omega t$$

Wavelength

Since e/m waves travel at a known velocity and vary sinusoidally, it is possible to consider how far a wave of given frequency (*f*) would travel during the execution of one cycle. Denoting the speed of light as (*c*), the wavelength (*W*) is given by:

$$W = c/f$$

From this, it is clear that the higher the frequency, the shorter the wavelength. Satellite broadcasting employs waves in the order of 10 GHz frequency so the order of wavelength can be calculated as follows:

$$W = (3 \times 10^8)) / (10 \times 10^9)$$
$$W = 3 \times 10^{-2} = 3 \ \text{cm}$$

In practice, the frequencies used are not necessarily a nice round figure like 10 GHz. Nevertheless, the wavelengths in present use invariably work out in terms of centimetres – they are, in fact, known as 'centimetric waves'. It is pertinent at this stage to question why such enormously high frequencies are used in satellite broadcasting? Before this can be answered, it is necessary to understand some fundamental laws relating to broadcasting of information, whether it be sound or picture information.

Carrier frequency

For simplicity, assume that it is required to transmit through space a 1000 Hertz audio signal. In theory, an electrical oscillator and amplifer could be rigged up and tuned to 1000 cycles per second and the output fed to a piece of wire acting as a primitive aerial. It is an unfortunate fact of nature that, for reasonably efficient radiation, a wire aerial should have a length somewhere in the order of the 'wavelength' (*W*) of 1000 Hertz. Using the equation given above:

$$W = c/f = (3 \times 10^8)/(10^3) = 3 \times 10^5 \quad \text{metres}$$
$$= 300\,000 \text{ metres which is about 188 miles!}$$

Apart from the sheer impracticality of such an aerial, waves at these low frequencies suffer severe attenuation due to ground absorption. Another important reason for using high frequencies is due to the considerations of bandwidth which is treated later.

The solution is to use a high frequency wave to 'carry' the signal but allow the 'intelligence' (the 1000 Hertz in our example) to modify one or more of its characteristics. The high frequency wave is referred to as the carrier (f_c) simply because it 'carries' the information in some way. The method of impressing this low frequency information on the carrier is called modulation. There are two main types, amplitude modulation (AM) and frequency modulation (FM).

Amplitude modulation (see Figure 1.2)

The low frequency modulating signal is made to alter the amplitude of the carrier at the transmitter before the composite waveform is sent to the aerial system. If the amplitude of the modulating signal causes the carrier amplitude to vary between double its unmodulated height and zero, the modulation is said to be 100 per cent. Terrible distortion results if the modulation amplitude is ever allowed to exceed 100 per cent.

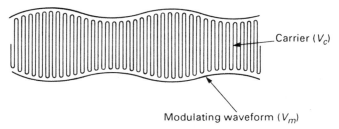

Carrier (V_c)

Modulating waveform (V_m)

Figure 1.2   *Amplitude modulation*

Modulation factor (*m*)

This is the ratio of modulation amplitude (V_m) to carrier amplitude (V_c):

$$m = V_m / V_c$$

When $m = 1$, the modulation is 100 per cent. Although 100 per cent modulation is an advantage, it is too dangerous in practice because of the possibility of overmodulation, so 80 per cent ($m = 0.8$) is normally considered the safe limit.

Sidebands

Although the modulating signal in Figure 1.2 is shown as a simple sinusoidal waveform, in practice it will be more complex. Thus the envelope of the waveform will be non-sinusoidal. Bearing in mind that only sinusoidal waveforms can be sent through space, there is clearly something odd to explain. This is where a little school maths comes in handy.

The unmodulated carrier sine wave has the instantaneous form:

$$v = V_p \sin \omega_c t$$

But the amplitude of this wave (V_p) is made to vary by the modulating frequency which causes V_p to have the form:

$$V_p = V_m \sin \omega_m t$$

Substituting this expression in the first equation gives:

$$v = V_m \sin \omega_m t \sin \omega_c t$$

In school, we were told that one of the trig. identities is:

$$\sin A \sin B = 1/2 \cos (A - B) - 1/2 \cos (A + B)$$

So it follows that the modulated carrier waveform splits up in space into three pure sinusoidal components:

1   The carrier frequency.
2   A frequency equal to the sum of the carrier and modulating frequencies. This is called the 'upper sideband'.
3   A frequency equal to the difference between the carrier and modulating frequency. This is called the 'lower sideband'.

Taking a simple numerical example, if the carrier frequency is 1 000 000 Hz and the modulating frequency is 1000 Hz, then the upper sideband is a 1 001 000 Hz sine wave and the lower sideband is a 999 000 Hz sine wave. In practice, the modulating frequency will seldom be anything as simple as a 1000 Hz sine wave but, more probably, may consist of speech or picture information which contains a complex mixture of frequencies. This does not invalidate the former reasoning. It just means that instead of single frequency upper and lower sidebands, there will be, literally, a band of sinusoidally varying frequencies either side of the carrier. For example, the music frequency spectrum extends from about 20 Hz to about 18 kHz so, to transmit high quality sound, the upper sidebands would have to contain a spread of frequencies extending from 20 Hz to 18 kHz above the carrier, and the lower sidebands, frequencies 20 Hz to 18 kHz below the carrier. Television transmission is more difficult because pictures have a far greater information content than sound. The sidebands must extend several MHz either side of the carrier. The wider the sidebands of a transmission, the greater space it will occupy in the frequency spectrum, so broadcast stations geographically close together must operate on frequencies well away from each other in order to prevent interference from their respective sidebands. Since television stations occupy several MHz in the spectrum, carrier frequencies are forced into ever higher and higher frequencies as the number of stations fight for space. There are several novel solutions to the overcrowding problem. For example, it is not essential to transmit both sidebands since all the required information is contained in one of them, providing of course the carrier is sent with it. Such transmissions are called SSB (single sideband). An even more drastic curtailment is to reduce the carrier amplitude at the transmitter to almost zero and use it to synchronize a locally generated carrier at the receiving end, a technique known as 'single sideband vestigial carrier' transmission.

Frequency modulation (FM)

Whereas amplitude modulation alters the envelope in the 'vertical plane', frequency modulation takes place in the 'horizontal plane' (see Figure 1.3). The amplitude of the carrier is kept constant but the frequency is caused to deviate proportional to the modulating amplitude.

 Constant amplitude carrier

Figure 1.3   *Frequency modulation*

Frequency deviation

The maximum amount by which the carrier frequency is increased or decreased by the modulating amplitude is called the frequency deviation. It is solely dependent on the amplitude (peak value) of the modulating voltage. In the case of satellite broadcasting, the signal beamed down to earth has a typical frequency deviation of about 16 MHz/V and the bandwidth occupied by the picture information is commonly about 27 MHz.

Modulation index (*m*)

This is the ratio of the frequency deviation (f_d) to the highest modulating frequency (f_m):

$$m = f_d / f_m$$

In contrast with amplitude modulation, the modulation index is not necessarily restricted to a maximum of unity.

Johnson noise

Any unwanted random electrical disturbance comes under the definition of noise. Such noise is all-pervading and is the worst enemy of the electronic designer. It begins in conventional circuitry, particularly with the apparently harmless resistor because, at all temperatures above zero kelvin (0°K), a minute, but not always negligible, emf (called Johnson noise) appears (and can be measured) across the ends. This is due to random vibration of the molecules within the body of the resistor and nothing whatever can be done to stop it. Although the following equation for Johnson noise is not particularly important in this text it is worth examining if only to grasp the strange connection between noise emfs and temperature.

RMS value of Johnson noise $= (4k \, tBR)^{\frac{1}{2}}$

where $t = 0°$ absolute temperature kelvin (room temperature may be taken as around 290°K)

$k =$ Boltzman's constant $= 1.38 \times 10^{-23}$
$R =$ the resistance in ohms
$B =$ the bandwidth of the instrument used to measure the emf.

Those with sufficient zeal to work out the noise from a one megohm resistor at room temperature would come up with a value of about 0.4 millivolts! This may seem small but it is relative, rather than absolute, values that are important. If the wanted signal is of the same order as this (in practical cases it could be much smaller) then the noise will swamp it out. Note from the equation, which incidentally is not restricted to man-made materials, the noise depends on the temperature, and the bandwidth of the 'instrument used to measure it'. Such an 'instrument' includes a broadcast receiving station! A high quality transmission has wide sidebands so the receiving installation must also have a wide bandwidth in order to handle the information in the sidebands. The occurrence of this form of noise entering the chain can seriously limit the quality of reception. Although Johnson noise has been used as an example, there are many other forms of noise (including ground and the man-made variety) which are treated in other parts of this book.

Signal to noise ratio (SN ratio)

This is the ratio of the desired signal emf to any noise emf present and should be as high as possible. If this ratio falls to unity or below, the signal is rendered virtually useless. (It is possible, but expensive, to use computer generated 'signal enhancement' techniques in some cases, but for domestic satellite broadcasting this is out of the question.)

Comparison of FM and AM

There are two features of AM which, in the past, have been responsible for its popularity:

1 The demodulation circuitry in the receiver, called 'rectification', is simple, requiring only a diode to chop off one half of the composite waveform and a low pass filter to remove the carrier remnants.
2 The side bands are relatively narrow so the transmission doesn't occupy too much space in the available frequency spectrum.

The most serious criticism of AM is that noise, at least most of it, consists of an amplitude variation. That is to say, any noise emfs present ride on the top of the envelope as seen in Figure 1.4. So, apart from meticulous design techniques based on increasing the S/N ratio, nothing much can be done about reducing noise without degrading signal quality by crude methods such as bandwidth reduction. FM, on the other hand, is often stated to be 'noise free'. This is not true! An FM transmission is as vulnerable to noise pollution as AM but, due to the manner in which the information is impressed on the carrier, much of the noise can be removed by the receiver circuitry. Since noise rides on the outside of an FM waveform, it is possible to slice off the top and bottom of the received waveform without destroying the information (remember that the information is inside the waveform rather than riding on the top and bottom). The slicing-off process is known as 'amplitude limiting'. A disadvantage of FM is the wide bandwidth required. FM is only possible if the carrier frequencies are relatively high. Fortunately, satellite broadcasting is well above 1 GHz so this is a trivial disadvantage. It cannot be denied that the circuitry required to extract the information from an FM carrier is, to say the least, awkward! The circuitry which performs this function is called an 'FM demodulator' which often takes bizarre forms. Among the various circuits that have been developed for FM demodulation are discriminators, ratio detectors and phased locked loops. This latter type is the most often used method and will be explained in Chapter 4.

Decibels (dB)

Decibels provide an alternative, and often more convenient, way of expressing a ratio between two powers. Instead of the actual ratio, the logarithm to base 10 of the ratio is used as shown below:

$$dB = 10 \log P_1/P_2$$

The sign of the result is positive if P_1 is greater than P_2 and negative if P_1 is less than P_2. To avoid the trouble of evaluating negative logarithms, it is a good plan always to put the larger of the two powers on top and adjust the sign afterwards in accordance with the above rule.

Examples: If $P_1 = 1000$ and $P_2 = 10$ then, dB $= 10 \log 1000/10 = 10 \log 100 = +20$ dB. (If P_1 was 10 and P_2 was 1000, the absolute value of dB would be the same but it would be written as -20 dB.) There are several advantages of using dBs instead of actual ratios:

1 Because the human ear behaves logarithmically to changes in sound intensity, decibels are more natural than simple ratios. For example, if the power output of an audio amplifier is increased from 10 watts to 100 watts, the effect on the ear is not 10 times as great.
2 Decibels are very useful for cutting large numbers down to size. For example, a gain of 10 000 000 is only 70 dB.
3 The passage of a signal from the aerial through the various stages of a receiving installation is subject to various gains and losses. By expressing each gain in terms of positive dBs and each loss in negative dBs, the total gain can be easily calculated by taking the algebraic sum.

Example: $(+5) + (-2) + (+3) + (-0.5) = 5.5$ dB.

A few of the more commonly used dB values are as follows:

Decibels (dB)	Relative power increase
0	1.00
0.5	1.12
1.0	1.26
2.0	1.58
3.0	1.99
6.0	3.98
12.0	15.85
15.0	31.62
18.0	63.09
21.0	125.89
50.0	100 000
100.0	10 000 000 000

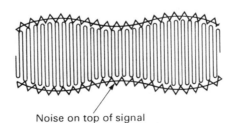

Noise on top of signal

Figure 1.4 *Noise on AM signals*

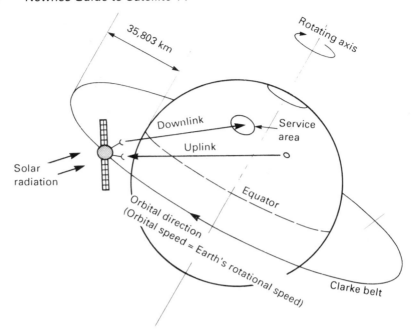

Figure 1.5   *The Clarke belt, uplink and downlink*

Voltage dB

Although dBs are normally used in conjunction with power ratios, it is sometimes convenient to express voltage ratio in dB terms. The equation in these cases is:

$$dB = 20 = \log \ V_1/V_2$$

The use of 20 instead of 10 is because power is proportional to the square of the voltage so the constant is 20 instead of 10.

Ku-band satellite TV

The European nations have almost exclusively adopted Ku-band (10.95 to 14.5 GHz) for the transmission of satellite TV signals. Likewise, the contents of this book are entirely biased toward Ku-band reception.

The Clarke belt

Back in 1945, Arthur C. Clarke, the famous scientist and science fiction novelist, predicted that an artificial satellite placed at a height of 35 803 km directly above the equator would orbit the globe at the same speed with which the earth was rotating. As a result, the satellite would remain stationary with respect to any point on the earth's surface. This equatorial belt, rather like one of Saturn's rings, is affectionately known as the *Clarke belt*. Any satellite within this belt is termed *geostationary*, and is placed in a subdivision known as an *orbital slot*. Signals are sent up to a satellite via an *uplink*, electronically processed and then re-transmitted via a *downlink* to make earth receiving stations. Figure 1.5 illustrates the points made.

The uplink

The uplink station is a fairly complex affair because not only do the signals have to be sent but they have to be sent at a differing frequency, usually in the higher 14 GHz band, to avoid interference with downlink signals. Another function performed by the uplink station is to control tightly the internal functions of the satellite itself (such as station keeping accuracy), although these technicalities need not concern us here. Up-links are controlled so that the transmitted microwave power beam is extremely narrow, in order not to interfere with adjacent satellites in the geo-arc. The powers involved are several hundred watts.

The downlink

Each satellite has a number of *transponders* with access to a pair of receive/transmit antennae and associated electronics for each channel. For example, in Europe, the uplink sends signals at a frequency of about 14 GHz, these are received, down-converted in frequency to about 11/12 GHz and boosted by high power amplifiers for re-transmission to earth. Separate transponders are used for each channel and are powered by solar panels with back up batteries for eclipse protection. The higher the power of each transponder then the fewer channels will be possible with a given number of solar panels, which in turn, is restricted by the maximum payload of launch vehicles as well as cost. Typical power consumption for a satellite such as ASTRA 1A is 2.31 kW with an expected lifetime of 12.4 years. Satellites are conveniently categorized into the following three power ranges:

1 *Low power* – These have transponder powers around the 20 W mark and are primarily general telecommunication satellites. Due to the low transmission power of each transponder they can support many channels with the available collected solar energy. Many of these transponders relay programme material for cable TV operators across Europe. Small numbers of enthusiasts eavesdrop on these broadcasts but unfortunately, receiving dishes of monstrous proportions are necessary for noise free reception, often in excess of 1 metre. This state of affairs is clearly not too popular with the general public who consider them, quite understandably, as dinosaurs of a past age. Even so, domestic TV reception is not the primary reason for

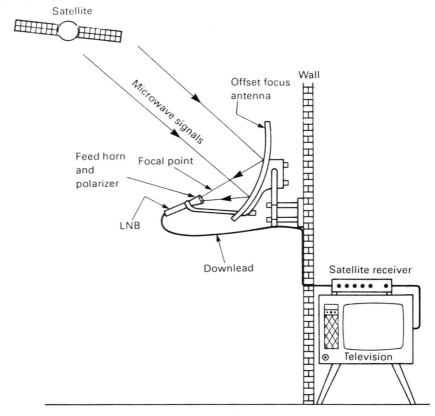

Figure 1.6   *Typical downlink configuration*

the existence of such high channel capacity satellites. Transponder bandwidths can vary.

2   *Medium power* – These satellites have typical transponder powers of around 45 W, such as those on board Astra 1A. Such satellites are now commonly termed semi-DBS (*direct broadcast service*) and represent the first serious attempt to gain public approval by offering the prospect of dustbin-lid-sized dishes of 60 cm diameter. About sixteen transponders are average for this class at the present time. Medium power European satellites usually operate in the frequency band 10.95 GHz to 11.70 GHz and form the *fixed satellite service* (FSS). The transponder bandwidths are commonly 27 MHz or 36 MHz. Some medium power satellites, such as the Eutelsat II series, also have a number of transponders that can be active in the 12.5 GHz to 12.75 GHz band, originally termed the business band service (BBS) by the International Telecommunication Union (ITU).

3   *High power* – These pure DBS satellites have transponder powers exceeding 100 W and have a correspondingly reduced channel capacity of around four perhaps five channels. The specified dish size

is minimal, about 30 to 45 cm in the central service area. These are perhaps the ideal size as far as the public are concerned and interest in satellite TV is expected to blossom as these come on stream. European transponder frequencies are in the band 11.70 to 12.50 GHz which is known as the *DBS band*. It has been agreed that the transponder bandwidths are 27 MHz.

Microwaves and the receiving site

The medium used to transmit signals from satellite to earth is *microwave electromagnetic radiation* which is much higher in frequency than normal broadcast TV signals in the VHF/UHF bands. Microwaves still exhibit a wavelike nature but inherit a tendency to severe attenuation by water vapour or any obstruction in the line of sight of the antenna. The transmitted microwave power is extremely weak by the time it reaches earth and unless well designed equipment is used, and certain installation precautions are taken, the background noise can ruin the signal. A *television receive only* (TVRO) site consists of an antenna designed to collect and concentrate the signal to its focus where a *feedhorn* is precisely located. This channels microwaves to an electronic component called a *low noise block* (LNB) which amplifies and down-converts the signal to a more manageable frequency for onward transmission, by cable, to the receiver located inside the dwelling.

Between the feedhorn and the LNB, a *polarizer* may be located, the function of which will be explained shortly. The complex of feedhorn, polarizer and LNB is often referred to collectively as the *head unit*. Figure 1.6 shows a typical downlink from a medium power satellite to domestic premises.

The antenna

The antenna or 'dish' is concerned with the collection of extremely weak microwave signals and bringing them to a focus. The surface must be highly reflective to microwaves and is based on a three-dimensional geometric shape called a *paraboloid* which has the unique property of bringing all incident radiation, parallel to its axis, to a focus as shown in Figure 1.6. There are two main types of antenna, one is called *prime focus* and the other *offset focus*. Briefly, a prime focus antenna has the head unit mounted in the central axis of the paraboloid whereas the offset focus configuration, as shown in Figure 1.6, has the head unit mounted at the focal point of a much larger parabaloid of which the observable dish is a portion. Antennae are normally made from steel, aluminium or fibreglass with embedded reflective foil. Antennae will be treated in more detail in Chapter 2.

Antenna mounts

The purpose of a mount is to point the antenna rigidly at any chosen satellite. There are two main types of mount, the *azimuth/elevation* (AZ/EL) mount which has simple horizontal and vertical adjustments and the *polar mount* which allows the dish to be tracked across the entire visible geo-arc, stopping at any chosen satellite. The first type AZ/EL is used mainly for fixed single satellite reception although a degree of multi-satellite reception can be provided in certain cases, such as the Astra plan to put three satellites in the same orbital slot. A single fixed dish will be able to receive signals from all three proposed spacecraft. Polar mounts are usually motorized and remotely controlled by an indoor positioner and are capable of receiving a fair number of satellites.

The feedhorn

The feedhorn, positioned at the focal point of an antenna, is a device which collects reflected signals from the antenna surface whilst rejecting any unwanted signals or noise coming from directions other than that parallel to the antenna axis. These are carefully designed and precision engineered to capture and guide the incoming microwaves to a *resonant probe* located at the front of the LNB. A feedhorn is really a *waveguide* whose basic theory has been known since the early days of radar, during the Second World War. They normally consist of rectangular or circular cross-section tubes and exhibit two important properties, dictated by waveguide theory. First, signals having wavelengths longer than half the internal dimensions are severely attenuated as the signal progresses down its length. Secondly, wavelengths shorter than the waveguides designed dominant mode become rapidly attenuated; thus the feedhorn behaves, in effect, like a band pass filter. The reason for the fluted horn is to match the free space impedance of the air with that of the waveguide. Feedhorns will be covered in a little more detail in Chapter 3.

Polarization

Current polarization techniques are classified as either linear or circular and are utilized for the following main reasons:

1   *Linear polarization* – A method to extend the number of channels that can occupy a given bandwidth, by using either horizontal polarization (*E* field horizontal to the ground) or vertical polarization (*E* field vertical to ground). This effectively doubles the number of channels that can be provided by a satellite since two channels can share the same frequency, providing they have opposite polarizations. In reality, these channels are staggered to minimize crosstalk (interference) between the two. Two jargon phrases which may cause confusion

with regard to polarization are *co-polarized channels*, meaning channels of the same polarization and *cross-polarized channels* meaning they are of opposite polarization. Figure 1.7 shows the two types of linear polarization.

2 *Circular polarization* – This method involves spinning the *E* field of the microwave signal into a spiral or corkscrew as shown in Figure 1.8. The two opposite polarizations this time are:

   (a)   Clockwise or right hand circular polarization (RHCP);
   (b)   Anticlockwise or left hand circular polarization (LHCP).

Although circular polarization can be used in much the same way as linear polarization, to extend the number of channels, it is more frequently used in high power DBS satellites for a different reason. DBS satellites usually have all their channels fixed at a single polarization either LHCP or RHCP. There is no need to extend the channel capability because this is limited more by power considerations than the numbers of channels. Adjacent DBS satellites in the geo-arc, due to their high power output, usually have opposite polarizations to reduce interference between signals on their earthward journey. Cross polarization leads to an equivalent suppression in interference in excess of 20 dB and is not noticeable to the viewer.

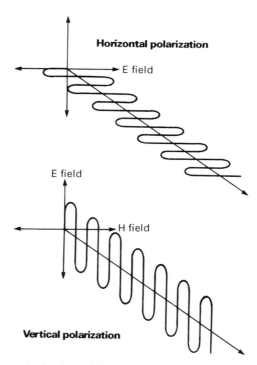

Figure 1.7 *Linear polarization of signals*

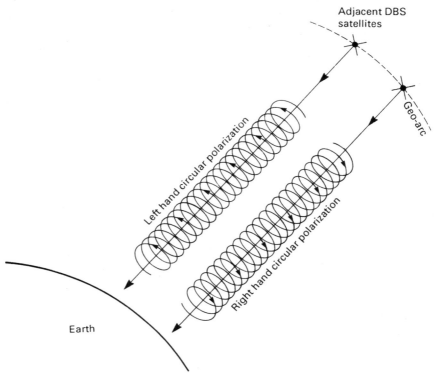

Figure 1.8   *Circular polarization from adjacent DBS satellites*

Polarizers

Polarizers are fitted either between the feedhorn and the LNB or inside the feedhorn itself and fall into three main categories.

1 *The V/H switch type* – These are simply a pair of probes positioned at 90 degrees apart. A solid state switch can select the output from one or the other depending on the selected polarization sense. This type is restricted to single satellite systems.

2 *Mechanical polarizer* – This type mechanically rotates a lightweight metal polarizer probe to lie in the plane of the required incoming electric field, that is to say the polarizer probe is vertical for receiving vertical polarized signals and horizontal for receiving horizontally polarized signals. The servo motor automatically positions the polarized probe according to the channel polarity selection stored in the receiver's memory. These polarizers, because mechanical movement is involved, have become less popular recently due to their inherent wear and subsequent unreliability. They are also liable to seizure in very cold weather and are often relatively slow in operation.

3 *Magnetic polarizers* – This is the favoured replacement for the mechanical type of polarizer; it consists of a ferrite former wound

with copper wire, into which a remotely controlled current is passed. The flow of this current generates a magnetic field which twists the incoming waves, depending on the polarization sense selected, to the orientation required for reception. This type of polarizer causes a slight attenuation of the incoming signal in the region of 0.3 dB. Because magnetic polarizers have no moving parts they are, in the main, reliable. The polarization reference plane is sometimes marked on the casing.

The low noise block (LNB)

The function of a LNB is to detect the weak incoming microwave signals via an internal tuned resonant probe, provide low noise amplification, and finally down-convert the whole block of frequencies to one suitable for cable transmission. It is common nowadays for the combination of feedhorn, polarizer and LNB to be manufactured as a single sealed unit. The entire assembly is often referred to as an LNB, for convenience, but it should be remembered that this is not strictly the case. The Marconi 'LNB' matched with the majority of low cost Astra receivers in the UK have this particular feature. All the components of a LNB are hermetically sealed against moisture.

Satellite receivers

The purpose of a satellite receiver is the selection of a channel for listening, viewing, or both, and transforming the signals into a form suitable for input to domestic TV and stereo equipment. Down-converted signals of about 1 GHz are fed by coaxial cable from the LNB to the input of the receiver. The various subsections of a receiver, which will be treated in Chapter 4, are listed below:

1 Power supply.
2 Second down-conversion and tuner unit.
3 Final IF stage.
4 FM video demodulator.
5 Video processing stages.
6 Audio processing stages.
7 Modulator.

It will be increasingly common to find TV sets with built-in satellite receivers designed to cover both the FSS and DBS band. These will probably be the norm in the years to come, especially so if the D-MAC standard becomes universally adopted. This system supports *conditional access*, which on receipt of payment, sends over the air customer addressing signals to enable decoding of programme material. Another advantage is the capacity for transition to high definition TV with an aspect ratio of 16:9. It is hoped that the familiar set top receiver, multiple decoders and spaghetti wiring may gradually disappear as the industry develops into the 1990s. If not, we may need a stepladder in the lounge to operate all the add on boxes of equipment.

Effective isotropic radiated power (EIRP) and footprint maps

An *isotropic radiator* is defined as one which radiates uniformly in all directions. For purposes of illustration it is perhaps better to use a light-bulb analogy. Imagine a 40 W light bulb suspended from a ceiling so as to be in line with a keyhole. An observer looking through the keyhole would see just a 40 W isotropic radiator. If a parabolic reflector from an old car headlamp is placed directly behind it, then the energy from the bulb will be reflected and magnified in one general direction, toward the keyhole, similar to a car's headlamp on main beam. To an observer, with a restricted field of view, the light source will appear as an isotropic radiator of much higher power. In other words, the effective power appears much higher than the actual power. This effect is somewhat similar to that which occurs with a parabolic transmitting antenna of a satellite. To a distant observer, which in this case is the receiving site antenna, the radiated power appears much higher than that of an isotropic radiator because the transponder antenna has a parabolic reflector and the receiving site antenna ('eye at the keyhole') has a restricted view of the transmitted beam. We know that the EIRP of the Astra 1A satellite is 52 dBW in the central service area, and that the transponder power is 45 W, therefore we can calculate the effective isotropic radiated power in watts as seen by the antenna.

$$EIRP = 10 \log (\text{effective power})$$
$$\text{effective power} = 10^{(EIRP/10)}$$
$$= 10^{(52/10)}$$
$$= 158\,489 \text{ W or } 158.5 \text{ kW}$$

From this we can calculate the magnification factor of the transponder's transmitting antenna:

$$\text{magnification} = 158\,489 / 45$$
$$= 3522 \text{ times}$$

Repeating the calculation for the BSB DBS satellite which has a transponder power output of 110 W and an EIRP value of 61 dBW in the central service area we get:

$$\text{effective power} = 10^{(61/10)}$$
$$= 1\,258\,925 \text{ W or } 1.25 \text{ MW}$$
$$\text{magnification} = 1\,258\,925 / 110$$
$$= 11\,445 \text{ times}$$

As with the lamp analogy the intensity of the beam will fall off as the distance from the main axis increases, since the beam will naturally diverge, in a conic fashion, with distance. A satellite *EIRP footprint* map is constructed by linking contours or lines through points of equal EIRP in the service area. The values will decrease away from the centre, as can be seen in Figure 1.9 which shows footprint maps for the four beams generated by the Astra 1A satellite. The above calculations show that large and unwieldy numbers start to emerge when we talk in effective power terms; this is why EIRP is measured in logarithmic decibel units relative to 1 watt. Remember that a 3 dB increase corresponds to a doubling of

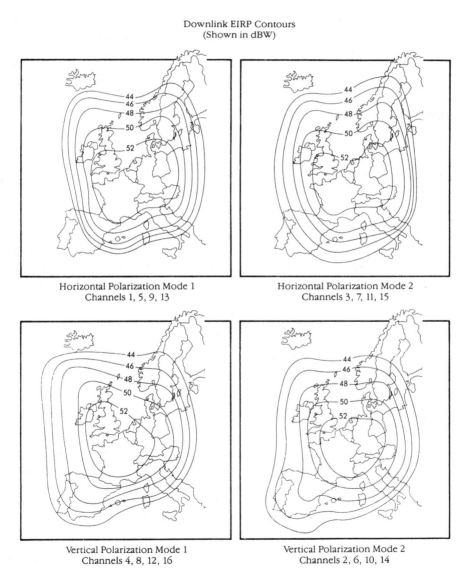

Downlink EIRP Contours
(Shown in dBW)

Horizontal Polarization Mode 1
Channels 1, 5, 9, 13

Horizontal Polarization Mode 2
Channels 3, 7, 11, 15

Vertical Polarization Mode 1
Channels 4, 8, 12, 16

Vertical Polarization Mode 2
Channels 2, 6, 10, 14

Figure 1.9   *Astra 1A footprint map*
(Source: Société Européenne des Satellites)

power. Therefore the apparent small increases in the values seen on footprint maps correspond to large changes in power levels. In this way relatively small numbers can be used to describe large power changes. Most footprint maps have this characteristic circular shape with EIRP levels falling off linearly away from the main service area.

Free space path loss

As the radiated signal of a transponder travels towards earth it loses power by spreading over an increasingly wider area thus diluting the signal strength. This effect is known as the *free space path loss* and the greater the distance the receiving site from the satellite the more it increases. Contributory factors include absorption of microwaves by gases and moisture in the atmosphere. The power density of signals, measured in watts per square metre, finally arriving at earth are extremely weak.

Rain attenuation

One of the major problems with satellite reception is rain, and to a lesser extent snow and hail. The weak incoming microwave signals are absorbed by rain and moisture, and severe rainstorms occurring in thundery conditions can reduce signals by as much as 10 dB (reduction by a factor of 10). Not many installations can cope with this order of signal reduction and the picture may be momentarily lost. Even quite moderate rainfall can reduce signals by 2 to 3 dB which is enough to give noisy reception on some receivers. Another problem associated with rain is an increase in noise due to its inherent noise temperature which is similar to that of the earth. In heavy rain depolarization of the signal can also occur resulting in interference from signals of the opposite polarization but same frequency. This effect is more noticeable with circular polarization.

Noise and its effects

Any body, above the temperature of $0°K$ or $-273°C$ has an inherent *noise temperature*. Only at absolute zero temperature does all molecular movement or agitation cease. At higher temperatures molecular activity causes the release of wave packets at a wide range of frequencies some of which will be within the required bandwidth for satellite reception. The warmer the body the higher the equivalent noise temperature it will have, resulting in an increase in noise density over the entire spectrum of frequencies. The warm earth has quite a high noise temperature of about $290°K$ and consequently rain, originated from earth, has a similar value. The characteristic appearance of noise on FM video pictures can be either black or bright white tear drop or comet shaped blobs ('sparklies') that appear at random on the screen. It is subjectively far more annoying than the corresponding snowy appearance of noise on terrestrial AM TV pictures. Video cassette recorder pictures, also frequency modulated, display annoying sparklies as a result of worn/dirty heads or faulty head amplifiers. Only relatively small amounts of FM noise can be tolerated.

2 Antennae

Introduction

The purpose of a satellite TVRO antenna is to concentrate weak incoming microwave signals from a distant satellite to a focus where they can subsequently be processed. The antenna should, ideally, reject any unwanted signals and noise. However, due to economic and aesthetic constraints, this may be compromised by various amounts for domestic equipment. Much research has gone into the design of microwave antennae over the years, mainly financed from military and tele-communications company budgets. Their offspring are now available with high specifications and low cost for today's domestic satellite reception.

The ideal antenna

Most Ku-band antennae are based on a particular shape called a parabola as shown in Figure 2.1. If this is rotated around its central axis, AB, by 360 degrees it becomes a three dimensional paraboloid which is the familiar dish structure we see. However, on paper we can only represent two dimensions conveniently, so the two dimensional representation shown must be mentally extrapolated into three. An ideal paraboloid has a unique property in that any incoming waves parallel to the main axis and arriving at the aperture are all focused to a single point in phase. Any waved entering at angles not parallel to the main axis are reflected so as to miss the focal point as shown in Figure 2.2.

It can be shown that an ideal, 100 per cent efficient, uniformly illuminated antenna of this type will have a power gain (G_a) as given in Equation 2.1.

$$G_a = 10 \ \log \left(\frac{\pi D}{W} \right)^2 \text{(dBi)} \tag{2.1}$$

where $\pi = 3.14159$
W = wavelength
D = aperture diameter

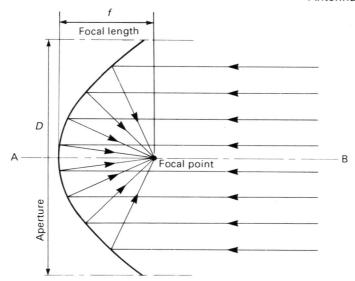

Figure 2.1 *Parabolic reflector*

From this it can be seen that the gain increases with the area of the antenna and also increases with the square of the frequency. It is important to remember that when power gain is expressed in decibel notation a 3 dB increase in gain represents a doubling of the power gain.

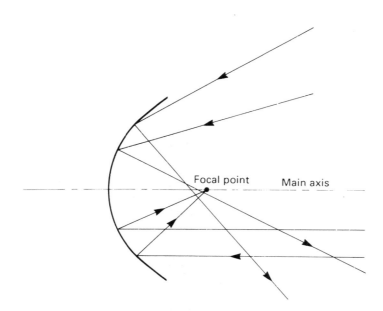

Figure 2.2 *Reflection of incoming waves*

Beamwidth

An ideal antenna should have a sharp pencil beam that targets only the chosen satellite and would be impervious to other stray signals or noise. In other words, it should have a narrow beamwidth. Beamwidth is traditionally measured in degrees at a point where the power level is −3 dB or half power. Equation 2.2 gives a good approximate value. The result can be expressed in degrees (°) or radians (rad) by choosing the appropriate constant (K).

$$-3\,\text{dB beamwidth} = KW/D \qquad\qquad (2.2)$$

where W = wavelength
D = antenna diameter
K = 70° or 1.2 rad

From Equation 2.2 it is seen that as the antenna diameter decreases the −3 dB beamwidth increases. Using this equation, a computer generated table has been produced to show how the 3 dB antenna beamwidth at 11 GHz varies with dish diameter. The results are given in Table 2.1 and are plotted graphically in Figure 2.3. Figure 2.4 shows an idealized detected radiation pattern for a 60 cm dish antenna with a single main lobe at a wavelength of 2.5 cm. Such an antenna would have a 3 dB beamwidth of about 2.9°. This corresponds to the width of the main lobe, represented

Table 2.1   *3 dB beamwidth values at 11 GHz for various diameter antennae*

Dish diameter (metres)	Beamwidth (degrees)
0.30	5.83
0.40	4.37
0.50	3.50
0.60	2.92
0.62	2.82
0.65	2.69
0.85	2.06
0.95	1.84
1.00	1.75
1.20	1.46
1.50	1.17
1.80	0.97
2.00	0.87
2.20	0.80
2.50	0.70
3.00	0.58
3.50	0.50
5.00	0.35
10.00	0.17

on the graph, at the −3 dB level and is an indication of the relative *field of view* of the antenna. This is more important the smaller the dish because if the beamwidth is halved, it gives an indication as to whether an adjacent satellite could possibly interfere with reception. For example, a 30 cm antenna would have a −3 dB beamwidth of 7°; if a second satellite happened to be within 3.5° east or west of the intended satellite and is transmitting on the same frequency and polarization, its signals could be received 3 dB down or at half power. Intolerable interference would result. If the antenna is not perfectly targeted the bias could well increase this effect. Furthermore, subjective tests have shown that interfering signals at the −11 dB beamwidth level are noticeable and values of −5 dB annoying. This lower 'potential interference beamwidth' is consequently wider due to the shape of the main lobe pattern.

Practical prime focus antennae

The ideal antenna is not obtainable in practice for the following reasons:

1   Waves, from whichever angle they enter the aperture, are diffracted at the edges of the dish and are scattered in all directions; some off-axis signals from adjacent satellites will undoubtedly converge on the focal point.

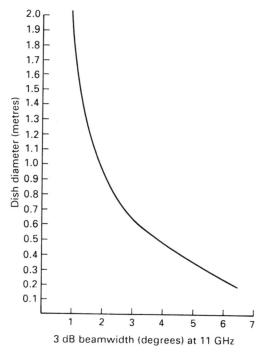

Figure 2.3   *3 dB beamwidth value at 11 GHz for various diameter antennae*

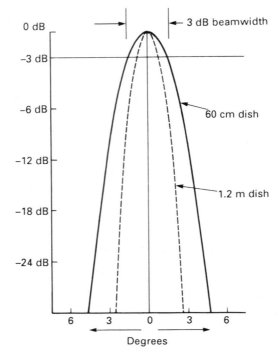

Figure 2.4 *Idealized detected radiation patterns*

2 Some of the parallel-to-axis wanted signals will be diffracted at the edge of the dish and will be lost from the focal point.
3 Surface irregularities cause reflection errors.
4 The head unit, mounted at the focal point, and its support structure will block, diffract and reflect incoming waves.
5 The head unit, occupying a larger space than a strict focal point will pick up off-axis signals.
6 Some background noise from the warm earth will be diffracted round the edge of the dish and converge on the focal point.
7 Some stellar background noise from space will converge on the focal point.
8 Microwave signals will be absorbed by the reflective surface of the antenna.

Some undesirable effects are shown in Figure 2.5, although various design techniques can minimize these to some extent. High standards of antenna pressing can reduce reflections from surface irregularities. Utilization of an offset focus configuration can eliminate blockage and reflection from the head unit and reduce the contribution of ground noise as explained later. The type of antenna described so far is called a 'prime focus' antenna and is losing popularity nowadays with the advent of small fixed dishes for semi-DBS and DBS satellite reception. In fact, there are very few prime focus antennae in the more popular packaged systems, although they remain in use with some motorized polar mount systems.

The foregoing contributory factors lead to the formation of side lobes in the detected radiation pattern. These side lobes, mainly determined by experiment, are capable of detecting interfering signals from satellites far removed from the intended source and can significantly contribute to the noise figure of the antenna. The first and largest of these side lobes appears at about 18 dB down, or lower, on each side of the main axis. Figure 2.6 shows the order of magnitude of these side lobes as the angle increases away from the main axis. Due to diffraction effects at the rim of the dish, the antenna is even capable of receiving signals and noise from behind. If the horizontal axis of Figure 2.6 was extrapolated round to 180° either side of the main axis these side lobes would become apparent. Fortunately, they are very much reduced in power compared to the main lobe. In fact, this is what constitutes a well-designed antenna. The main lobe should be as narrow as possible for the size of the dish and the side lobes should be reduced to a minimum value, relative to the main lobe. Paying attention to the effects listed above can help to achieve this aim.

Offset focus antennae

The offset focus configuration is rapidly gaining popularity with the onset of semi-DBS and DBS satellite services. Figure 2.7 shows that the

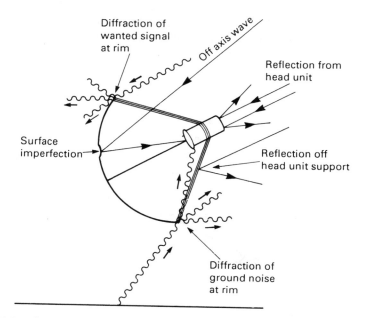

Figure 2.5 *Some undesirable effects*

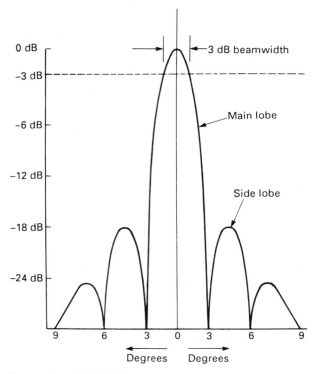

Figure 2.6   *Formation of side lobes*

offset focus configuration is really the top half of a parabola. The focal point is at the norm of a much larger parabola (extra shown by dotted line). These antennae have certain advantages over the prime focus type as can be seen in Figure 2.7. Firstly the head unit is out of the line of sight

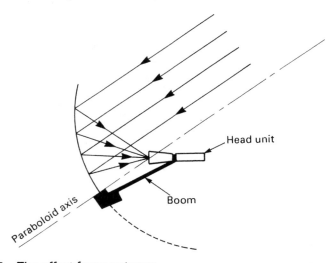

Figure 2.7   *The offset focus antenna*

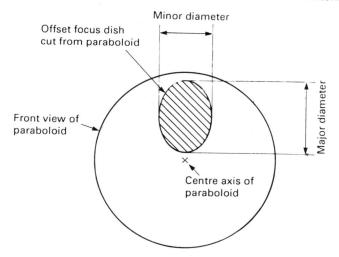

Figure 2.8   *Offset dish cut from large parabola*

of incoming microwave radiation thus eliminating the effects of signal blockage. Secondly the head unit is inclined upwards away from the earth and toward space, so reducing the contribution of ground noise to the total system noise. Thirdly, because the dish has a more vertical orientation accumulated snow, bird's nests or other debris will tend to slide off.

It was stated earlier that an offset dish is 'really the top half of a larger parabola'. This is not strictly true. The width is also restricted as can be seen in Figure 2.8. The offset dish can be imagined as a section cut from a much larger diameter paraboloid. The familiar common shape of an Astra dish can be seen shaded within the front view of the parabola. Some manufacturers like to deviate from the norm and chop off the top and bottom to give a more rectangular appearance. This, of course, does not imply that manufacturers make them by this method. It is just an aid to visualization. Offset focus dishes of this type do not have a circular beamwidth pattern as do prime focus antennae. The minor diameter will inherit a larger beamwidth than the major diameter so the result will be a flattened elliptical spotlight beam as seen in Figure 2.9. It follows from this that we would expect the elevation of the dish to be slightly more critical to adjust than the azimuth since the beamwidth is narrower. Hence the importance of mounting the antenna mast or wall bracket absolutely vertical.

The Cassegrain antenna

Figure 2.10 shows another possible configuration for domestic satellite reception, called the Cassegrain antenna. However it is little used because of the added expense of the hyperbolic subreflector although it

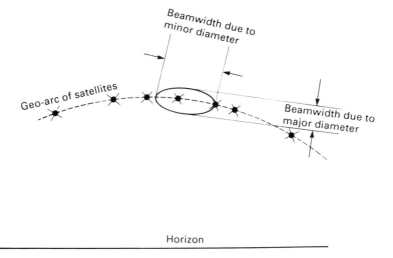

Figure 2.9   *The flattened elliptical beam of an offset focus antenna*

does have certain advantages. The profile may be slimmer, since the subreflector intercepts reflected waves before their normal prime focal point and re-reflects them back to a rear mounted head unit. The main disadvantage is that the subreflector blocks some of the incoming signal, however this may be overcome by using an offset design.

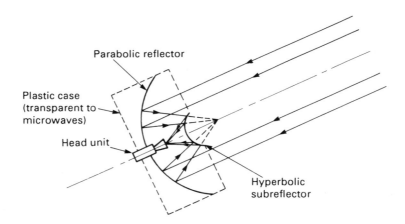

Figure 2.10   *The Cassegrain antenna*

The flat antenna

With the introduction of high power, DBS satellites there is much current research into the concept of the flat antenna. BSB's 'squarial' is one such project which may or may not come to fruition. Instead of focusing the incoming radiation to a point, it is possible to collect it in an array of small aerial elements over a flat surface. The radiation power received by the simple aerial elements, in the form of slots, can be added, in a rear mounted conductive transmission network, and taken to a common output. Unfortunately, at the time of writing, no such antenna has been successfully launched in the European domestic market. The alleged advantages of this type are small size, light weight and ease of installation.

Antenna efficiency

Antenna efficiency is a measure of the percentage amount of incoming signal finally reaching the head unit. Antenna efficiencies generally range from 55 to 70 per cent for domestic satellite reception. The main factors determining efficiency are again outlined below:

1 Some of the parallel-to-axis wanted signals will be diffracted at the edge of the dish and will be lost from the focal point.
2 Surface irregularities can cause reflection errors.
3 The head unit, mounted at the focal point, and its support structure will block, diffract and reflect incoming waves.
4 There will be a certain amount of absorption of microwave radiation by the reflective surface of the antenna.

Not a lot can be done about the effects of (1) since this is governed by fundamental physical laws. However, an offset focus configuration can eliminate the effects of (3). Careful choice of materials and precision engineering can reduce the effects of (2) and (4). Surface irregularities are quoted by antenna manufacturers as a 'worst case' parameter called 'RMS deviation'. The lower this value, the better the quality of construction of the dish.

Practical antenna gain

The equation given for the gain of an ideal antenna, Equation 2.1, needs to be modified to take into account antenna efficiency (P). The modified equation is simply Equation 2.1 multiplied by the value $P/100$,

$$G_a = 10 \log \frac{(\pi D)^2 \times P}{100 \times W^2} \text{ (dBi)} \tag{2.3}$$

where $\pi = 3.14159$
$D =$ antenna diameter
$P =$ antenna efficiency
$W =$ wavelength

To show how antenna gain varies with dish diameter for a range of efficiencies, a computer generated table using Equation 2.3 is reproduced in Table 2.2. The frequency chosen is 11 GHz and would give near

Table 2.2   *Antenna gain for a range of dish diameters and efficiencies*

Dish diameter (metres)	Antenna efficiency					
	55%	60%	65%	70%	75%	80%
0.30	28.17	28.55	28.90	29.22	29.52	29.80
0.40	30.67	31.05	31.40	31.72	32.02	32.30
0.50	32.61	32.99	33.34	33.66	33.96	34.24
0.60	34.20	34.57	34.92	35.24	35.54	35.82
0.62	34.48	34.86	35.21	35.53	35.83	36.11
0.65	34.89	35.27	35.62	35.94	36.24	36.52
0.85	37.22	37.60	37.95	38.27	38.57	38.85
0.95	38.19	38.56	38.91	39.23	39.53	39.81
1.00	38.63	39.01	39.36	39.68	39.98	40.26
1.20	40.22	40.59	40.94	41.26	41.56	41.84
1.50	42.15	42.53	42.88	43.20	43.50	43.78
1.80	43.74	44.12	44.46	44.78	45.08	45.36
2.00	44.65	45.03	45.38	45.70	46.00	46.28
2.20	45.48	45.86	46.21	46.53	46.83	47.11
2.50	46.59	46.97	47.32	47.64	47.94	48.22
3.00	48.17	48.55	48.90	49.22	49.52	49.80
3.50	49.51	49.89	50.24	50.56	50.86	51.14
5.00	52.61	52.99	53.34	53.66	53.96	54.24
10.00	58.63	59.01	59.36	59.68	59.98	60.26

worst case values for Ku-band antenna gain. The results for a 60 per cent efficient antenna are plotted graphically in Figure 2.11.

Noise

What is noise?

Any signal received is combined with an element of noise which degrades the overall performance. Therefore the relationship is:

Signal = wanted signal + noise

To receive good quality pictures the noise should be reduced to a minimum. The higher frequency components of noise affect satellite antennae and consist mainly of the following:

1 *Stellar noise* – This is the wide bandwidth radiation caused by the energy conversion in stars and is a subject of study by radio astronomers. The contribution is low compared with ground noise and is more independent of antennae elevation. This noise predominantly enters the antennae via the main lobe.

2 *Ground noise* – At all temperatures above absolute zero degrees (0°K or −273°C) excitation of molecules in the warm earth contribute a wide bandwidth range of interfering signals known as ground noise or thermal noise. This increases the lower the elevation of the

antennae due to diffraction effects at the edges of the dish, as shown in Figure 2.5, and the noise mainly enters via the antenna side lobes.

3 *Man-made noise* – This noise emanates from man's electrical and electronic apparatus in the vicinity of the antenna. For example, the switching on and off of fluorescent lights, drills, motor car ignition circuits, etc. These all emit a wide frequency range of radiation due to high transient voltages. Again this mainly enters via the antenna side lobes.

Antenna noise

The above noise contributions are conveniently grouped into a quantity known as *antenna noise* and this is the figure normally quoted in antenna manufacturer's specifications. As mentioned earlier, most noise is produced by excitation of molecules above absolute zero therefore noise increases with temperature. This is why noise is often quoted in the form of an equivalent *noise temperature*. The unit of measurement is therefore degrees kelvin (°K). The figure of 290°K is taken as the nominal figure for the warm earth. This equates to 17°C. We can now arrive at a simple equation to describe antenna noise which is given at Equation 2.4.

$$T_{ANT} = T_{STELLAR} + T_{GROUND} + T_{MAN\text{-}MADE} \quad °K \qquad (2.4)$$

The contributions from stellar noise and man-made noise are relatively low in comparison to the major component from ground noise. Therefore it is expected, from what has been discussed, that an antenna

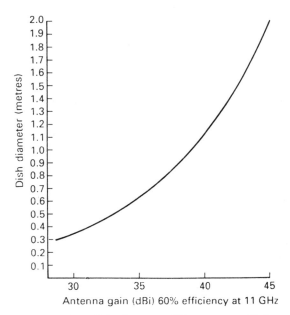

Figure 2.11 *Antenna gain v dish diameter (60 per cent efficiency)*

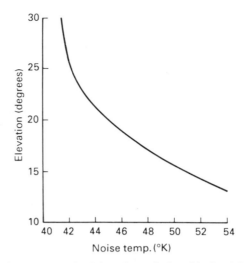

Figure 2.12   *Typical antenna noise/elevation relationship for 1.2 m dish*

with low side lobes in relation to the main lobe would, for a given diameter, constitute a good low noise antenna design. The lower the beamwidth of an antenna, the narrower is the main lobe and thus the closer spaced are the side lobes to it. It follows that the level of immunity to noise in general will increase with the antenna diameter and this is found to be the case in practice. Inclining the head unit away from the ground and toward space as the result of the offset focus configuration will also reduce the ground noise component. This is one of the reasons why the majority of small diameter antennae, below one metre, incorporate the offset feed to partially counteract the increase in antenna noise due to low antenna size at low latitudes. Figure 2.12 shows a typical antenna noise/elevation relationship for a 1.2 metre dish.

Focal length to diameter ratio and noise

Since transmission is effectively the reverse of reception the concept will be described for transmission, otherwise the terms used may be confusing. By convention, the same terms are used for both but unfortunately they do not convey much when visualizing a TVRO antenna. Think of the head unit as a directional microwave source (a feed) and the dish concentrating and reflecting the signal out toward space. A paraboloid antenna can be shallow or deep depending on the depth of slice taken. Figure 2.13 shows the extremes of the focal length to diameter ratio. It is difficult to get uniform illumination over such a wide angle with configuration (a) and the corresponding effect is called *under illumination*. On the other hand it is difficult to catch a high proportion of radiation on to the reflector with configuration (c), the corresponding effect being called *over illumination*. Usually, the configuration giving the maximum gain is slightly cheaper than (b), at a point where the reflector can be uniformly illuminated. Figure 2.13(b) is where the focal point is in the aperture plane, and parabola geometry dictates that this happens when the *f/D* ratio is 0.25. Dishes with low *f/D* ratios tend to have lower amplitude side lobes as a result of the tapering of illumination (under illumination) towards the rim of the dish. Returning to reception, rather than transmission, the same trends still apply, deeper dishes tend to inherit lower side lobes than do shallow ones thus decreasing the vulnerability to ground noise. That is to say, the head unit is more shielded from extraneous noise and does not detect excessive noise from beyond the edge of the dish. However both extremes may produce unacceptable gain. In practice, *f/D* values commonly lie between 0.25 and 0.6. The same principles apply to offset focus dishes but it must be remembered from earlier discussion that the focal point of the parent paraboloid is applicable. The design of the feed is more difficult than for prime focus types since microwaves are collected from only a portion of the paraboloid. Typical *f/D* ratios for offset designs are 0.5 to 0.6. Another consideration for the domestic market is that shallow dishes tend to be more aesthetically pleasing than deeper ones.

Antenna mounts

The purpose of a mount is to rigidly and accurately target an antenna onto a particular satellite or range of satellites. There are two basic types of mount for an antenna:

1   The azimuth/elevation mount (AZ/EL).
2   The polar mount.

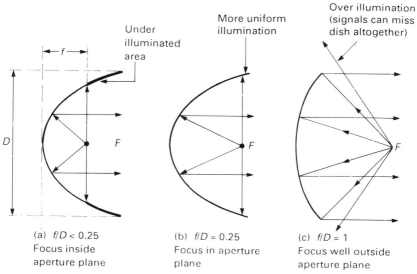

(a) *f/D* < 0.25
Focus inside
aperture plane

(b) *f/D* = 0.25
Focus in aperture
plane

(c) *f/D* = 1
Focus well outside
aperture plane

Figure 2.13   *Focal length to diameter ratios (f/D)*

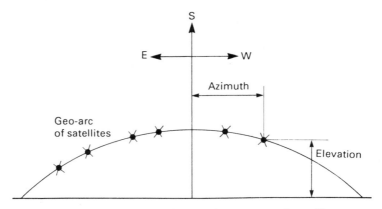

Figure 2.14   *How AZ/EL settings relate to the geo-arc of satellites*

Fixed AZ/EL mounts

As implied by its name, this type of mount enables antenna movement in two directions and is normally used to target a single fixed satellite or group of satellites in the same orbital slot. Once targeted the mount can be permanently clamped to a specific azimuth and elevation setting. This simple type of mount is currently the most popular in the domestic electronics field for small, fixed semi-DBS and DBS antenna. The advantages of this type of mount are low cost and ease of installation and maintenance. The chief disadvantage is that only one small area of the geo-arc is targeted. Figure 2.14 shows how the azimuth and elevation settings relate to the geo-arc of satellites in the northern hemisphere.

Motorized AZ/EL mounts

Although very rare, it is possible to encounter motorized AZ/EL mounts that are capable of multi-satellite targeting by remote control. These are considered the 'Rolls Royce' of mounts and are capable of targeting any satellite in the geo-arc with unsurpassed accuracy. Sophisticated dual digital servo mechanisms acting under microcomputer control drive a pair of geared motors which can target the dish to any pre-programmed AZ/EL position stored in memory. However, this type of mount is unlikely to be popular, at the present time, due to the high costs involved.

The polar mount

The polar mount is the most popular and cheapest method of multi-satellite reception using a single antenna since its movement is restricted

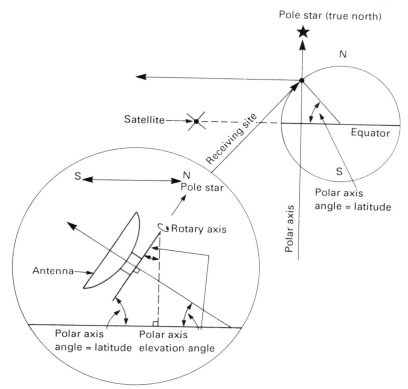

Figure 2.15 *The standard polar mount*

to one axis. The polar axis is parallel to a line intersecting the north and south geographical poles and at any point on the earth's surface the polar axis angle is equal to the latitude of the receiving site. If the polar axis angle of the mount is set to equal the latitude as shown in Figure 2.15, the antenna will point straight out from the earth into space in a plane parallel to the site latitude. Swinging the dish around the polar axis will trace out a circular arc of the sky as shown in Figure 2.16.

From Figure 2.16 it is evident that the standard polar mount has serious shortcomings in tracking the geo-arc. This is resolved to an acceptable

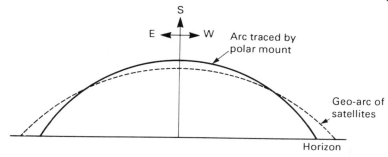

Figure 2.16 *Arc traced by standard polar mount*

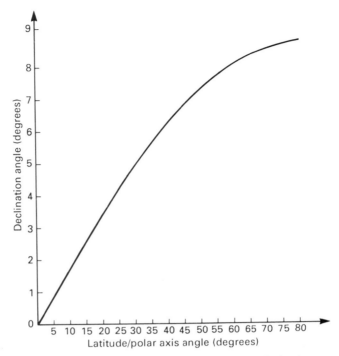

Figure 2.17 *How declination angle increases with site latitude*

level by tilting the antenna forward onto the geo-arc by the introduction of a fixed declination offset angle which can be calculated for any particular latitude using Equation 2.5. The constants are the equatorial radius (km) and the height of the satellite arc over the equator (km).

$$\text{Declination angle} = \arctan \frac{6378 \sin B}{35\,803 + 6378\,(1 - \cos B)} \text{ (degrees)} \qquad (2.5)$$

where $B =$ site latitude

Figure 2.17 shows the relationship between declination angle and latitude. At the equator, the declination angle will be zero because the polar axis angle or latitude is zero degrees (dish pointing straight up), but as the site position increases with latitude so will the necessary declination offset angle up to a maximum of a little over 8.5°. Above latitudes of 81° satellite reception is not possible because the entire geo-arc is over the horizon. Figure 2.18 shows the new geometry. When the polar axis is set up in a true north–south orientation, a further declination angle is added to the polar axis angle. The most southerly highest point of the geo-arc, or the apex elevation is perfectly targeted and a reasonable match to the geo-arc is obtained. However, at extreme azimuths there is still a small tracking error as shown in Figure 2.19.

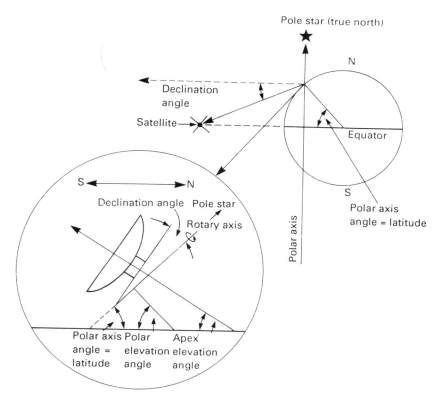

Figure 2.18 *Polar mount with declination offset*

The modified polar mount

To improve the geo-arc tracking even further, engineers have come up with the modified polar mount geometry. It is strange that it is called 'modified' since the addition of a declination angle is, in itself, a modification. Nevertheless, the basic principle is to tilt the polar axis very

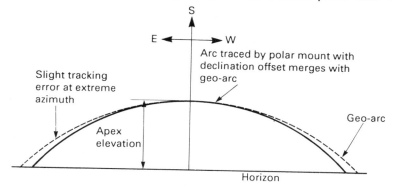

Figure 2.19 *Arc traced by polar mount with declination offset*

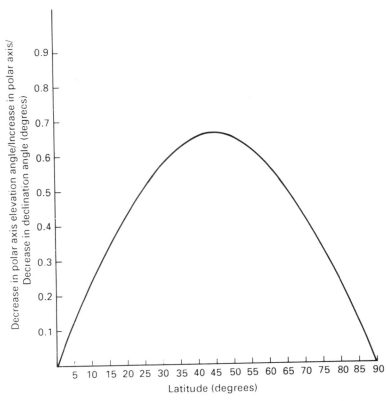

Figure 2.20   *Correction factors for modified polar mount geometry*

slightly forward at the apex position (due south or highest point of the geo-arc) thus marginally increasing the polar axis angle. An equal reduction in the declination angle is effected to counteract this so that the apex elevation remains the same when pointing due south. The result of this modification is that tracking errors at extreme azimuths are resolved and tracing of the entire geo-arc is possible with a high degree of accuracy. All polar mount antennae allow for this fine adjustment of tracking, the practical details of which will be covered in the later installation chapters. Figure 2.20 shows the necessary correction factors to the polar axis and declination angles for various latitudes.

Motorized polar mounts

Up till now, we have assumed that a polar mount is adjusted by hand to target any particular satellite in the geo-arc. This is the case with some primitive installations. More commonly, however, the dish can be set by remote control using an *actuator* and an indoor unit called a *positioner* which is sometimes built into multi-satellite receivers. A *linear actuator* is commonly a motor driven arm, of 30 cm throw, which operates from a

36 V supply. The control system, shown in a conceptually simplified form in Figure 2.21, works like this: on selecting a particular satellite, the current position count is compared with that programmed into memory and the motor, and subsequently the antenna, are driven in the appropriate direction by extending or retracting the actuator arm. The current position count is continuously compared with the value programmed into memory until such time as the two counts match, at which point the supply to the motor is cut. The position transducer or sensor in the feedback loop can be a Hall-effect transistor, reed relay or, more commonly, an optical counter, depending on the particular design. Luckily, the positioner has inbuilt safeguards to stop the actuator from being driven beyond certain limits. For average domestic use, the current requirements for the motor are typically 2 A and the maximum load is often quoted at around the 225 kg region. This leaves a good safety margin for the majority of installations.

Antenna construction

Most modern antennae are constructed using one of the following three main techniques:

Spinning

Flat sheet metal is placed onto a parabolic mould and the whole assembly spun. A forming tool or roller then gradually changes the shape of the sheet until the familiar dish shape emerges. A large range of dish sizes can be made from the same parabolic mould and are consequently cheap to produce.

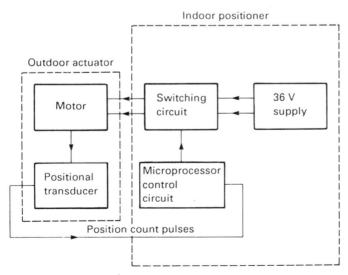

Figure 2.21 *Simplified actuator feedback control*

Pressing

Flat sheet metal is pressed into the required shape using a hydraulic press with a male and female die. Water is often utilized to help produce a good smooth and reflective surface. The process is similar to that of pressing car body panels. Different pairs of die need to be used for each antenna size.

Foil embedded in fibreglass

This method uses lightweight metal reflective foils embedded in a solid fibreglass paraboloid dish. The foils are placed in a mould and then injection moulding techniques complete the process. Fibreglass antennae are slightly less efficient than their solid metal counterparts since microwaves need to penetrate the fibreglass layer reflect and then re-emerge. Some of these will be absorbed in the process. This method of construction is common with offset feed designs.

Painting

A common enquiry by customers is 'can we paint the dish a different colour?'. Although not recommended, the answer is yes, as long as the same principles are applied as that in manufacture. The paint should be applied as smoothly as possible, any bumps or drips may cause reflection errors. The paint used should not be optically reflective such as metallic paints or gloss finishes otherwise the sun's radiation may become focused on the head unit and cause problems. Always use 'vinyl matt' finish paints which exhibit lower solar reflection properties. The amount of microwave absorption and reflection errors using this type of paint is minimal in practice and no loss of performance should be noticed.

3 Head units, cables, line amplifiers and connectors

Head unit

A head unit is a convenient group name for the assembly positioned at the focus of a dish antenna and comprises the following component parts:

1 Feedhorn.
2 Polarizer.
3 Low noise block (LNB).

The basic operation of these components has been outlined in Chapter 1. However, the treatment in this chapter is more concerned with why feedhorns and LNBs are needed at all!

Why do we need a feedhorn and LNB?

Signals passing through a length of coaxial cable suffer attenuation per unit length due to:

1 Dielectric losses in the material necessary to support the inner conductor.
2 Skin resistance due to the finite diameter of the inner conductor.
3 Radiation loss due to the coaxial cable operating as an aerial.

All these losses increase with signal frequency. However, by correct choice of cross-sectional dimensions and materials, the attenuation due to these losses is acceptable providing the signal frequencies are not too high! It is unfortunate that broadcast signals from the current satellites are in the 11/12 GHz range and coaxial cables, except in very short lengths, are unable to cope. There are two ways of overcoming the problem:

1 Employ frequency conversion techniques at the aerial head to lower the frequency sufficiently for subsequent handling by coaxial cable.
2 Abandon coaxial cable altogether and pass the signal down the inside of a hollow metal tube – in other words, use waveguides!

Since waveguides can pass gigahertz signals with negligible attenuation, the ideal solution would be to use them exclusively to provide the path between the aerial (the 'dish') on the outside of the wall or roof and the receiver inside the house. Unfortunately, waveguides demand precision engineering and the component cost would be prohibitive. Apart from the cost, it is doubtful if house owners in an up-market estate would like to see a long length of piping snaking down the wall only to disappear through the window frame and continue along the skirting boards of the lounge. The solution, as always when there are conflicting requirements, is a compromise: a short stub of waveguide to pass the satellite signals to the first stage frequency converter (positioned close to the dish), and high grade coaxial cable for the rest of the run, down the wall to the receiver. The frequency converter section is called the LNB and the short waveguide stub and its connection to the focal point of the dish is known as the feedhorn.

Basic waveguide operation

It is not necessary to delve deeply into the horrifying complexities of waveguide theory because they form only a small part of the total transmission path in commercial satellite installations. However, those cursed with an insatiable appetite for knowledge should consult one of the many textbooks on the subject – for example, the old, but still eminent Defence Ministry publication, *The Services Textbook of Radio, Volume 5, Transmission and Propagation* published by HMSO. The following treatment only provides a rough outline of the essential features of waveguides. A word of advice; some texts, mainly American, specify the A dimension of a rectangular guide as the major dimension but in the UK, the larger dimension is often taken as the B dimension. Another point is that modes H_{01}, H_{02} ... etc. are sometimes referred to as TE_{10}, TE_{20} ... etc. This non-standardized terminology can sometimes lead to considerable confusion when studying waveguide theory from a selection of text books.

Rectangular waveguides

A signal passing along a coaxial cable conforms to conventional circuit practice, that is to say, it is described in terms of voltage (V) appearing across the inner and outer conductors and the current (I) flowing along the conductors. In a waveguide, as the name implies, the signal remains in the form of an electromagnetic wave and is therefore more properly considered in terms of an electric field (E) and a magnetic field (H). It is essentially a wave disturbance, trapped within the confining walls of the guide. However, the guide dimensions must be chosen to satisfy the following boundary rules imposed by electric and magnetic fields:

1   An E field can never be parallel to a perfectly conducting surface if close to that surface.

2 An H field can never be at right angles to a perfectly conducting surface when close to that surface.

Because of these restrictions and because the wall of a waveguide is, for all practical purposes, a perfect conductor, it appears that a wave can never propagate straight down a metal tube but must travel by a series of reflections from wall to wall – it bounces along. (See Figure 3.1(a).)

The bouncing angle depends on the cross-sectional dimensions of the guide. For reasons given later, the longer dimension (B) is the more critical and is normally designed to be greater than a half wavelength and less than a full wavelength. Within these two limits, the B dimension determines the bouncing angle. The longer the B dimension, subject to the upper limit, the less times the wave will bounce (wide bouncing angle). The wave suffers slight attenuation during each bounce, so the fewer the bounces the more efficient the propagation down the guide. (See Figure 3.1(b).) If the B dimension is shortened down towards the half wavelength limit, the number of bounces increase dramatically. In fact when B is exactly a half wavelength, the wave bounces backwards and forwards in the same place and is said to be in an *evanescent* mode; in plain English, it won't come out the other end! (See Figure 3.1(c).) It would seem from the foregoing that it would be a good thing to have the B dimension as near as possible to a full wavelength in order to minimize the number of bounces the wave has to make during its passage down the guide. Unfortunately, there is another unwanted effect which occurs when the B dimension is too near the full wavelength limit – the danger of allowing so-called 'higher order modes' to be propagated. To ensure predictability, waveguide techniques are directed towards the

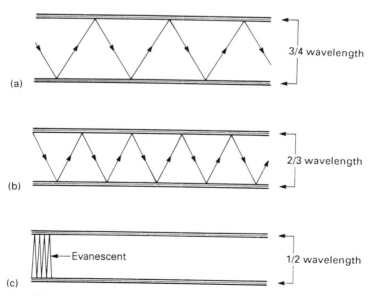

Figure 3.1 *Effect of B dimension on bouncing angle*

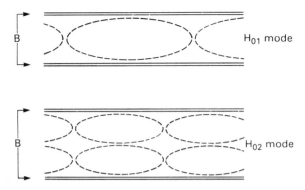

Figure 3.2   *Magnetic field patterns*

propagation of a simple wave pattern known as the 'dominant mode'. Such a mode demands the smallest possible guide cross-section and is known as the H_{01} mode. By ensuring the B dimension is not too near the half wavelength limit, only the dominant mode can propagate since higher order modes (H_{02} and beyond) become evanescent. Figure 3.2 illustrates the difference between the magnetic field patterns in the dominant mode and the second high order mode. The conflicting requirements of wide bouncing angle and avoidance of higher order modes leads to a B dimension compromise in the region of three-quarters of a wavelength. The 11 GHz band corresponds to a wavelength of approximately 2.7 cm so the B dimension of a rectangular guide is chosen to be around 2 cm. A waveguide thus has the advantage of filtering out unwanted signals other than the designed wavelength region.

The A dimension is not critical but, by definition, it must be shorter than the B dimension otherwise the wave could slip round and the *E* and *H* field directions would be unpredictable. In the dominant mode, the *E* field lines lay across the guide axis, parallel to the A dimension so if A is too short and the signal strength is exceptionally high, the electric stress could cause arcing across the guide walls. Fortunately, the *E* field strength at a satellite receiving dish is far too weak to worry about arcing. This danger only crops up during the design of high powered centimetric transmitters.

Waveguide impedance

As all technicians will know, a coaxial cable has a definite characteristic impedance which is independent of its length and normally fixed at 75 ohms. Technicians will also be aware of the unpleasant effects of a coaxial cable feeding a mismatched load impedance. It is therefore not surprising to learn that waveguides also have a characteristic impedance and require matched loads before they will function correctly. In the dominant mode, the characteristic impedance of a rectangular guide is dependent on the B dimension, and because of the restrictions mentioned above is normally in the region of 600 ohms. At the receiving dish, whenever a section of waveguide is used, however short, there is a problem arising from the inherent mismatch between the waveguide impedance and the impedance of free space. The waves collected at the focal point of the dish if collected by the waveguide must somehow be matched to the waveguide. It is difficult to visualize the concept of the impedance of free space because how can 'nothing' have an impedance? The answer to this seeming paradox is tied up with the permittivity (k_0) and the permeability (μ_0) of free space and the nature of electromagnetic propagations. All such waves, whether radio, television, x-rays or gamma rays have the following properties:

1　They all consist of an *E* field and an *H* field, the amplitudes of which vary sinusoidally as they move through space.
2　The *E* and *H* fields are always at right angles to one another and travel in a direction at right angles to both fields.
3　The ratio of the *E* field to the *H* field is always exactly 120 π ohms or 377 ohms approximately. (See Figure 3.3.)

It is this last property which is mysterious and why we can make the following statement:

The characteristic impedance of free space is 377 ohms.

We can understand the reasoning behind this if we first note that the *E* field is a *voltage* concept and is considered in terms of volts per metre while the *H* field is a *current* concept and is considered in terms of amps per metre. Since the ratio of *E* to *H* fields in free space is 377 ohms, then the ratio of *V* to *I* must also be 377 ohms. In symbols,

$$E/H = \frac{V/d}{I/d} = V/I = 377$$

Since the ratio of voltage to current has the dimensions of impedance, it is not illogical to conclude that free space has an impedance of 377 ohms. Strictly speaking, the waves in the vicinity of the dish are not in perfectly free space but this is little more than an academic distinction.

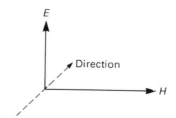

Figure 3.3　*E, H and direction vectors*

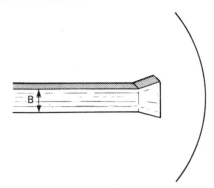

Figure 3.4   *Horn feed*

The horn aerial

It is clear that a mismatch will occur if the open end of a rectangular waveguide is just left at the focal point of the dish. It will certainly collect power from the dish but there will be a mismatch between free space impedance (377 ohms) and the waveguide impedance (about 600 ohms). This will lead to the partial reflection of the incoming microwave signal back to the antenna. A quantity, known as the voltage standing wave ratio (VSWR), is a measure of how much signal is reflected back and lost due to impedance mismatch. Under matched conditions, the rms voltage should be the same at all points along the length of the transmission path. Mismatching causes voltage nodes (voltage minima) and anti-nodes (voltage maxima) to appear at fixed points on the path. The ratio of an antinode to a node is called the VSWR. VSWR should ideally approach 1:1 but normally 1.5:1 and below is acceptable in practice. It was stated above that the impedance of a guide is reduced as the B dimension is increased so one way out of the muddle is to widen the tip of the B dimension as shown in Figure 3.4. The extremity of the guide now acts as a horn aerial at the focal point of the dish. There are several exotic ways of terminating the guide at the other end, including a projecting pin aerial or probe placed at a point in the guide corresponding to an *E* field maxima. This is normally located in the throat of the LNB.

Circular guides

It is also possible to use guides with circular cross-section although there are some disadvantages, the main one being the difficulty of predicting the plane of the *E* and *H* fields. Because of the symmetry of a circular structure, there is nothing to prevent the wave-pattern slipping round. The wave might start with, say, the *E* field lines at a certain angle but a few inches along the guide, the pattern could twist round a fraction. Good design can only proceed if parameters are predictable so an unpredict-able slip in the *E* field is not conducive to good design! However, if the length is short, as indeed it would be in this case, there may not be room for such a slip to occur so circular guides can be used. The dominant mode in a circular guide is the E_{01}. One advantage of circular guides is that they tend to be cheaper to produce. Often a transition from circular to rectangular waveguide is encountered along the path to the aerial probe.

Polarizers

Polarizers, treated briefly in Chapter 1, can vary in construction and can be classified into the following main types:

1   *V/H switching type* – Two probes, one for vertical polarization and one for horizontal polarization are positioned 90° apart. A simple solid state switching arrangement selects either the vertical output or the horizontal output. These units have very low insertion losses with good cross-polar isolation. The main disadvantage is that they are only suitable for either single satellite reception or reception of multi-satellites in the same orbital slot such as the Astra cluster.
2   *Ferrite or magnetic devices* – These devices are embedded in the feedhorn assembly. The incoming wave is twisted according to the current flowing through the windings. The inclusion of such a device leads to a typical insertion loss of about 0.3 dB. However, since the amount of wave twisting also depends to some extent on frequency, they can produce poor results unless some method of trim for different channel frequencies is allowed for on the receiver. A remote skew adjustment (see later) which can be stored for each channel is normally all that is required to compensate for this.
3   *Mechanical motor driven types* – A motor physically rotates a probe according to the polarization sense selected. These devices are comparatively rare these days and work under remote servo control from the receiver.

   The vast majority of fixed satellite service transmissions use linear polarization techniques. However, with the advent of circular polarization on DBS satellites operating in the 11.70 to 12.50 GHz band, it is necessary for manufacturers to modify the construction of a linear polarizer by embedding a small rectangle of dielectric material, at 45° to the horizontal, in the throat of the feedhorn or polarizer. This enables circular polarization to be resolved by a linear polarizer. Other more elaborate methods can also be used to distinguish between LHCP and RHCP. For example, one of two probes set at right angles can have its output delayed by a quarter wavelength relative to the other, the resulting vector addition of the signals detects one circular polarization scheme and reversal of the delay detects the other. Single fixed satellite DBS packages only need resolve one sense of circular polarization which greatly simplifies polarization circuitry and thus cost and ease of installation.

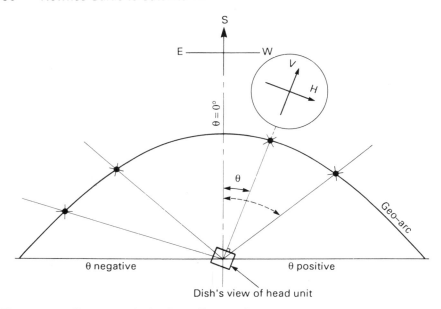

Figure 3.5   *Skew or polarization offset angles*

Skew

An angle known as skew, or polarization offset, needs to be taken into account with linear polarization. The reason for this is best visualized by referring to Figure 3.5. As satellites are removed from due south in the geo-arc, the angle of vertical polarization is twisted away from true vertical. The angle, θ, thus increases for satellites at the extremities of the geo-arc. For fixed satellite installations the compensatory adjustment is performed by simply rotating or twisting the head unit assembly in its mounting to minimize depolarization of the signal and reduce inter- ference from cross-polarized channels. With multi-satellite systems skew adjustments for each required satellite (or channel) may be either pro- grammed into memory, for subsequent recall, or manually controlled by a knob on the receiver/positioner. In this case skew is algebraically added to the reference plane of the polarizer. A further use for this adjustment is to fine trim the skew for each channel on the same satellite using either magnetic or mechanical polarizers. Detailed programming of skew adjustment varies widely so read the manufacturer's instructions carefully.

The low noise block (LNB)

The low noise block is a fairly complex piece of equipment but its basic operation is as follows: the short stub of waveguide is continued to a resonant probe or aerial located in the LNB throat. At this probe the incoming microwave signals are converted to minute electrical signals which are subsequently amplified and block down-converted to a frequency more suited for onward transmission by coaxial cable. The overall gain of a LNB is typically within the range 50 dB to 60 dB. Efforts to exceed this figure have been found to be influenced by the law of diminishing returns. A word of warning, the internal probe aerial should never be touched or tampered with because it is delicate and easily damaged.

The whole assembly is hermetically sealed against the ingress of moisture. If moisture should get into the unit, corrosion, then subsequent failure, may result. Some head units combine feedhorn polarizer and LNB into a single unit, others have component parts which need to be bolted together. In the latter case silicone rubber 'O' rings are fitted between the connection flanges to prevent the seepage of moisture into the feedhorn and LNB sections. The first IF output from a LNB is generally via an 'F' connector. This should be waterproofed by the installer with either self-amalgamating tape or a rubber weatherproof boot. The sub-sections of a simplified LNB are shown in Figure 3.6.

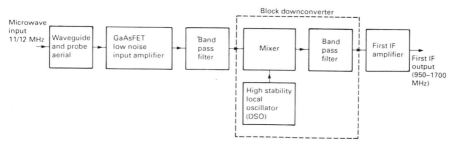

Figure 3.6   *Simplified schematic of a LNB*

Low noise input amplifier

The low noise input stage of a LNB is designed using gallium arsenide field effect transistors (GaAsFET) devices. This technology has certain advantages over their silicon counterparts at microwave frequencies. These are:

1   GaAs can withstand higher working temperatures due to the relatively large band gap.
2   Electron mobility is much higher in GaAs thus shortening transit times and increasing the maximum frequency of operation.
3   Low power GaAs amplifying devices operating at average outdoor temperatures have low leakage currents and dissipate little heat. This significantly contributes to the inherent low noise temperature figures obtained with these devices.

Most current low cost LNBs for domestic packages inherit noise figures

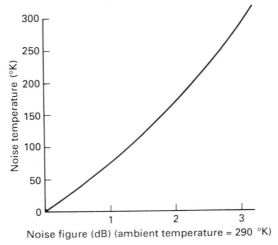

Figure 3.7   *Noise figure v noise temperature (ambient temperature 290° K)*

of about 1.5 to 1.8 dB (noise temperatures 119.6°K to 148.9°K at 290°K ambient temperature).

HEMT LNBs

A further refinement of GaAs technology is the high electron mobility transistor (HEMT). These devices, as their name implies, have even higher electron mobility leading to increased frequency capability, reduced thermal generation, and consequently lower noise temperatures when used in the input amplifier stage. This type of LNB is currently the top-of-the-range device and can produce noise figures as low as 1.0 dB (noise temperature 75.09°K and 290°K ambient). However, due to the extra expense, these are usually provided as an optional extra at increased system cost. As prices continue to fall, these devices may soon become commonplace in low cost equipment. Up to a certain degree, a lower noise LNB can compensate for a slightly undersized antenna. It must be stressed that this tradeoff cannot be pushed too far.

Noise figure and noise temperature

In manufacturer's specifications for equipment it is normal to quote the noise figure of a LNB in dB this can be converted to its corresponding noise factor by the following relationship:

$$F_{LNB} = 10^{(NF/10)} \text{ where NF is the noise figure of the LNB.}$$

This noise factor value can be substituted in the following equation to obtain the equivalent noise temperature, which is an alternative way of specifying the noise performance of a LNB.

$T_{LNB} = 290(F_{LNB} - 1)$ where F_{LNB} is the noise factor of the LNB.

For convenience, a computer generated table, Table 3.1, has been produced showing the relationship between noise figure and noise temperature at an ambient temperature of 290°K. The results are plotted in Figure 3.7.

To obtain the equivalent noise figure from the noise temperature use the following two reversal equations:

$$F_{LNB} = 1 + (T_{LNB}/290) \text{ and, } NF = 10 \log (F_{LNB})$$

Block down-converters

Another important function of the LNB is to change the frequency of the incoming signals to a more manageable frequency for onward transmission to the receiver. Coaxial cable has its limitations at high frequencies as mentioned at the beginning of this chapter so frequencies in the 10.95 to 11.70 GHz fixed satellite service band or 11.70 to 12.50 GHz DBS band are far too high for transmission by normal coaxial cable. A frequency changer or down-converter consists basically of a local oscillator and mixer which is conceptually similar to that used in the common superheterodyne radio receiver. However, the technology required to keep the fixed frequency local oscillator sufficiently stable to shift a whole 750 MHz group of microwave channels to a lower range proved difficult. With the advent of dielectric stabilized oscillators (DSO) this process has become the standard. For the fixed satellite service band in Europe, the group or block of channel frequencies is by convention down-converted to the range 950 to 1700 MHz using a low side local oscillator of 10 GHz. Potential interference from UHF TV transmitters and other civil transmissions dictates the choice of this down-converted band and unfortunately, this necessitates the use of higher grade cables than standard UHF coax. The main advantages of block down-conversion are:

1   More than one receiver, fed from a common antenna and head unit, can independently receive any of the selected co-polarized channels in the group.
2   The channels are less likely to drift off tune since the channel selection circuitry is indoors where ambient conditions are relatively constant.

Practical down-conversion

The Astra system

The sixteen channel group from the Astra 1A satellite is arranged as shown in Figure 3.8, and extends between 11.20 GHz and 11.45 GHz, a relatively small section of the 10.95 GHz to 11.70 GHz band. This group of

Table 3.1   Noise figure v noise temperature (ambient temperature 290°K)

Noise figure (dB)	Noise temperature (degrees K)
0.00	0.00
0.10	6.75
0.20	13.67
0.30	20.74
0.40	27.98
0.50	35.39
0.60	42.96
0.70	50.72
0.80	58.66
0.90	66.78
1.00	75.09
1.10	83.59
1.20	92.29
1.30	101.20
1.40	110.31
1.50	119.64
1.60	129.18
1.70	138.94
1.80	148.93
1.90	159.16
2.00	169.62
2.10	180.32
2.20	191.28
2.30	202.49
2.40	213.96
2.50	225.70
2.60	237.71
2.70	250.01
2.80	262.58
2.90	275.45
3.00	288.63

frequencies, as part of the larger block, are mixed with a local oscillator running at 10 GHz to provide a down-converted group of channel frequencies extending from 1200 MHz to 1450 MHz, which is a comparatively small subsection of the first IF frequency range from the LNB (950 MHz to 1700 MHz). This is the group of Astra 1A channel frequencies which is ultimately fed via the coaxial cable to the input of the indoor receiver unit. Figure 3.9 shows the channels which are down-converted from Astra 1A, depending on which polarization sense is selected. The Astra 1B and 1C satellite channels will be down-converted to other slots in the 950 MHz to 1700 MHz spectrum making 48 channels in all from three satellites positioned in the same orbital slot. Most head units and receivers designed for Astra reception should be able to accommodate

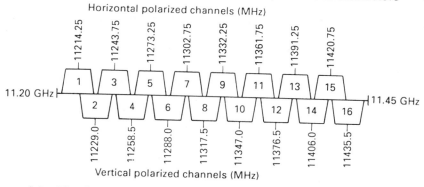

Figure 3.8 *The Astra 1A downlink plan*

these extra channels when they become available, although some have insufficient preset memory to store all the channel selection data.

When purchasing non-European equipment it is important to check that the input frequency range of the LNB corresponds with those used in Europe and that the 1st IF output group of frequencies match that accepted by the chosen receiver.

Eutelsat II series

The medium power Eutelsat II series of satellites, unlike Astra, will have different orbital slots. The first is located 13° east of south. The downlink plan is somewhat more complicated than Astra's because they are capable of covering not only the 10.95 GHz to 11.70 GHz band but also the 12.5 GHz to 12.75 GHz band. The latter band is above the DBS band (11.70 GHz to 12.50 GHz) which has been earmarked by the French Telecom I and II series of satellites. The Eutelsat II series have seven wideband 72 MHz transponders and nine 'narrowband' 36 MHz transponders, all with linear polarization, making sixteen transponders per satellite. Of these sixteen, five can be switched out from the 10.95 GHz to 11.70 GHz band to

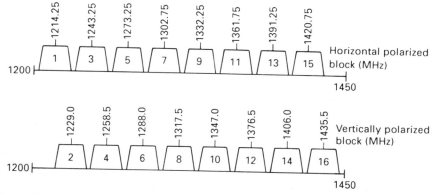

Figure 3.9 *Down-converted frequencies for Astra 1A*

the 12.5 GHz to 12.75 GHz band as the need arises. The downlink plan, Figure 3.10, shows the five switchable channels; suffix (e) shows them in the lower band and suffix (t) shows them in the higher frequency band. With this flexibility, Eutelsat II systems can operate up to twelve transponders in the 10.95 GHz to 11.70 GHz band or up to ten in the 12.50 GHz to 12.75 GHz band where four transponders are permanently active. A low side local oscillator operating at 10 GHz in a standard 10.95 GHz to 11.70 GHz band LNB would again down-convert the lower frequency band channels within a 1st IF range of 950 MHz to 1700 MHz. Unlike the Astra series a multi-satellite motorized system would be required to receive all the planned Eutelsat II series satellite transmissions.

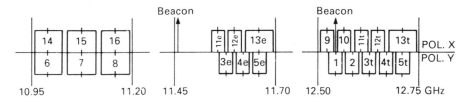

Figure 3.10   *Eutelsat II downlink plan (Source: Eutelsat)*

BSB: Marcopolo 1

The BSB Marcopolo 1 satellite at 31°W has a relatively simple downlink plan. Five 27 MHz bandwidth channels are centred at 11.785 02 GHz, 11.861 74 GHz, 11.938 46 GHz, 12.015 18 GHz and 12.0919 GHz. The estimated life of Marcopolo 1 is ten years and all channels employ circular polarization. Due to the restricted availability of chip sets for conditional access, reception is restricted to the UK and Eire only. It will not be possible for multi-satellite systems to be equipped for BSB reception at the present time.

Cables

The down-converted group of satellite channels, commonly known as the 1st IF, occupy a band of frequencies from 950 MHz to 1700 MHz for the fixed satellite service in Europe. Unfortunately, these frequencies are far too high for ordinary UHF TV cable to be used except in very short runs of a few metres. In practice, cable runs are considerably longer than this, so a lower loss, better quality cable should be selected. The attenuation figure per 100 metres, at the usable frequency, is perhaps the most important parameter as far as the installer is concerned, although a lower attenuation figure coaxial cable is usually accompanied by an increase in diameter and subsequently cost. Clearly, for the domestic market, a compromise must be reached where an acceptable diameter cable at reasonable cost is selected.

Cable attenuation and line amplifiers

Cable attenuation is commonly measured in dB per 100 metre length and this increases with frequency. Figure 3.11 shows the frequency v attenuation/100 m relationship for a common cable type, CT100. The noise introduced to the system by excessively long cable runs, or poor choice of cables, has a similar appearance on a TV picture to that associated with a poor terrestrial UHF aerial installation. A grainy or snowy picture results rather than the 'sparklies' produced by satellite antenna pointing errors. Subjectively, the latter type of noise is far more annoying to the viewer. The maximum cable attenuation that can be tolerated, without noticeable degradation of picture quality, is in the region of 12 dB to 15 dB. Thus a scan through the tables, presented in this chapter, will show which cable is most suited to a particular run.

For the average wall mounted single satellite installation, the most often used cable is CT100 (H109F). This allows a maximum cable run of about 45 m which is more than sufficient for the vast majority of cases, which in practice, rarely exceed 20 m. For longer runs, the fitment of inexpensive line amplifiers can compensate for cable attenuation but it is important to remember that it will be fruitless to fit one in order to reduce sparklies from a poor input. This is because the noise level injected into the cable, as well as the signal, are amplified which results in no overall improvement in the signal to noise ratio. Fitting a larger antenna or a lower noise LNB is the only way to cure this problem. The fitting of line amplifiers, every 30 m or so, can often be a cheaper solution, for occasional long runs, rather than stocking less-used, higher quality cables. Line amplifiers obtain their power from the LNB voltage feed, so extra wiring is avoided. Another important parameter, as far as the installation

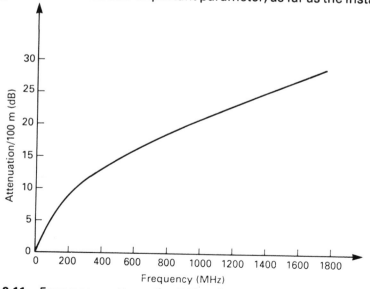

Figure 3.11   *Frequency v attenuation/100 m for cable type CT100*

Table 3.2　*Coaxial cables manufactured by Volex Raydex*

Type	Number of polarizer conductors	Impedance (ohms)	Attenuation/ 100 m at 1750 MHz (dB)	Sheath diameter (mm) A	B	C
CT 100	0	75	28.3	–	6.45	–
CT 125	0	75	23.6	–	7.80	–
SAT 100	0	75	28.6	–	6.65	–
RA 519	0	50	17.5	–	10.30	–
RA 521	0	50	22.5	–	7.85	–
SAT 1001	1	75	28.3	11.00	6.85	4.15
SAT 1002	2	75	28.3	13.00	6.85	4.25
SAT 1003	3	75	28.3	13.00	6.85	4.50

technician is concerned, is the minimum bending radius of the cable. As a general rule, the minimum bending radius of a coaxial cable should be about ten times its sheath diameter or undue attenuation may result. Cables are normally supplied in black as this colour provides maximum protection from ultra-violet radiation.

Cables suitable for direct burial

Manufacturers produce their cables in a choice of either PVC (polyvinyl-chloride) or PE (poly-ethylene) sheaths. PE sheathed cables may be directly buried, but it is inadvisable to use PVC sheathed cables in any underground situation. Volex Radex have further produced a patented form of bonded laminated sheath called RBS (Raydex Bonded Shield). The flexible, bonded outer jacket has several advantages over other cables for direct burial. Firstly, the jacket is impact and abrasion resistant and secondly, good pull strength and slip characteristics make it ideal for use in underground ducts.

Cabling requirements for single satellite installations

There appears to be no standardization with regard to cabling requirements for the various manufacturer's fixed satellite packages. For example the first Amstrad/Fidelity and Ferguson Astra packages use single coax. The IF signals are fed down the cable from the dish and a d.c. voltage is fed back up the cable from the receiver to supply the LNB. This d.c. voltage can be varied to operate an inbuilt V/H polarization switch. The corresponding Grundig package uses coax with an additional polarizer lead to alter the polarity of the polarizer. The LNB supply of 15 V is fed up the coax and a further 12 V supply cable is used to control the polarizer: zero volts for vertical polarization and 12 V for horizontal polarization. The earth return is via the coax braid. First launched Tatung and ITT models use coax with two separate polarizer leads. Rarely encountered motor driven polarizers will need three extra conductors. Combination cables incorporating these extra conductors in the same sheath are available from Volex Radex distributors, and broadly equivalent versions manufactured by Pope cables, from Webro (Long Eaton) Limited. See Appendix 2 for addresses. These special multiple cables are relatively costly, so a sometimes used, but far less professional solution, is to run a separate cheap multi-core cable for the polarizer requirements in conjunction with normal quality coaxial cable, such as CT100 or H109F.

Volex Radex range of cables for single satellite installations

Table 3.2 shows the parameters of cables, suitable for single satellite installations, from Volex Radex. Included in the table, are 50 ohm types that may be occasionally needed to match certain LNBs and receivers. However, the 75 ohm type is by far the most commonly used.

The SAT 1000 series are a range of composite cables with single, twin or triple polarizer leads to suit any single satellite TV installation. They all employ a 'figure-eight' construction as shown in Figure 3.12, and each retains its own sheath when separated for termination. Each polarizer conductor is again separately insulated.

Either CT100 or SAT 100 can be stocked for installations incorporating the V/H switch type of polarizer. In order to wire up all the other possible polarizer configurations, clearly SAT 1003 is a universal cable, since any unused conductors can be either snipped off or parallel connected. However, since motor driven polarizers are comparatively rare these days, perhaps SAT 1002 may be a reasonable alternative.

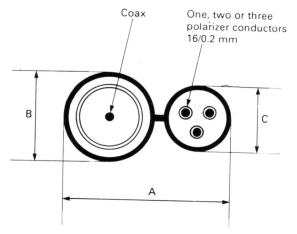

Figure 3.12 *Cross-section of SAT 1000 series cables from Volex Radex*

Pope range of cables for single satellite installations

A range of equivalent cables are manufactured by Pope Cables. The official distributors are Webro (Long Eaton) Ltd. Generally speaking H109F is equivalent to CT100 and H47 is equivalent to CT125. A universal cable, shown in cross-section in Figure 3.13, capable of any polarizer wiring combination, is type H142A (all in a single PVC sheath) or H142B (figure-eight sheath). This cable incorporates type H125 coaxial cable, broadly equivalent to CT125 from Volex Radex, with three insulated 0.5 mm conductors for linear polarizer wiring. Again, any unused conductors can be snipped off or connected in parallel.

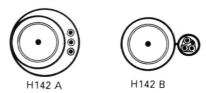

H142 A   H142 B

Figure 3.13   *Universal cable type H142 for additional polarizer wiring (Source: Webro (Long Eaton) Ltd)*

If your business is restricted to mainly fixed dish installations, then it is recommended that H109F and H142 are kept in stock to meet all present eventualities.

Multi-satellite motorized installations

The cabling requirements for multi-satellite motorized systems are slightly more complicated and usually comprise the following:

1 Normal quality, coaxial cable for feeding the block down-converted signals to the receiver. The 15 to 24 V LNB supply is also simultaneously fed via this cable.
2 Three polarizer conductors for mechanical polarizers or one/two for magnetic polarizers.
3 Actuator cable for the dish drive comprising two conductors for the motor power plus three additional conductors for the position sensor.

These requirements can all be wired separately, but specially produced universal cables for such installations are available which enable an easy, neat and professional job to be performed.

Pope multi-satellite cable

The requirement may be met by using H142 cables for (1) and (2), and using H143 cable for (3). The cable H143 consists of two PVC insulated 1.4 mm² stranded copper conductors for the actuator motor power plus three, 0.5 mm PVC insulated solid copper conductors, for the position sensor needs. The cable cross-section is shown in Figure 3.14.

Figure 3.14   *Cable type H143 for actuator wiring (Source: Webro (Long Eaton) Ltd)*

For an even neater job, there is a combined cable, type H144, which consists of H142 and H143 integrated into the same PVC sheath, and available in two configurations, figure-eight or ribbon, as shown in Figure 3.15.

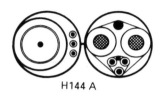

Figure 3.15   *Universal multi-satellite system cable type H144 (Source: Webro (Long Eaton) Ltd)*

If all forms of installation are likely to be undertaken then it is recommended that H109F, H142 and H144 cables, or their equivalents, are stocked. In this way any job can be performed neatly and with the minimum of effort. The minimum reel size is usually 250 metres.

Volex Radex multi-satellite cable

Volex Raydex produce a similar universal cable for multi-satellite installations, type K1005. This cable is available in a flat form, four component configuration and is shown in cross-section in Figure 3.16. The coaxial section of the cable is available in 75 ohm CT125 or 50 ohm RA521.

Connectors

The F connector is now established as the standard for coaxial terminations and is available in many forms. Some need to be crimped with a

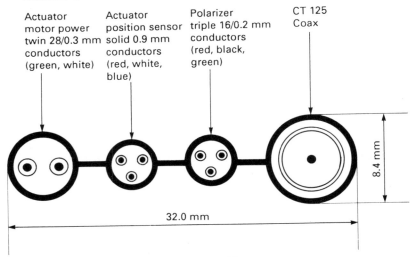

Figure 3.16   *Cross-section cable type K1005*

special tool or pliers and others are simply twisted on to the end of the stripped cable. I have found that the 'twist-on' type of connector is by far the most versatile and easiest to fit and can literally be fitted in less than thirty seconds. The connectors require a standard coaxial strip length and are available in a range of internal diameters to suit most cables. Due to the tapering of the entry guide a wide range of cable thicknesses can be used for each size. As a general rule, the internal diameter of the chosen connector should be in the region of 0.5 mm to 1 mm smaller than the outside cable diameter to ensure good strain relief without excessive distortion of the cable. Twist-on connectors are available from CPC Ltd (see Appendix 2) together with a whole range of adaptors and accessories for any requirement out of the ordinary. The main advantage of this type over the crimped variety are outlined below.

1 Completely re-usable (no scrap or wastage).
2 Single piece construction.
3 Quick and easy to fit.
4 No special tools or soldering required.
5 Do not corrode (nickel plated brass).
6 Tapered entry guides ensure a good contact and high strain relief.

Some installers prefer the crimp type of connector but it is really a matter of personal choice. Waterproofing characteristics of F connectors are not really relevant to choice, since all outside connections should be either overwrapped with self-amalgamating tape or protected by a weatherproof rubber boot.

4 Satellite receivers

Introduction

The purpose of a satellite receiver is the selection of an individual channel, from the down-converted block, for viewing. The received signal must also be processed into a form suitable for interfacing to a conventional TV set and/or stereo equipment. Receivers may be incorporated as a subsection of a conventional TV set or built as a separate unit and contain, at least, the following blocks of circuitry.

1   Power supply.
2   Satellite tuner/demodulator unit.
3   Video processing circuits.
4   Audio processing circuits.
5   UHF modulator.

Jargon terms and abbreviations

Inevitably, a number of jargon terms and abbreviations have crept into telecommunications subjects which may be confusing to the newcomer. The commonly used terms appropriate to the understanding of satellite receiver schematic diagrams are defined and explained below.

AGC (automatic gain control) – This is a term used to describe a method of automatically backing off the strength of strong signals relative to weak ones thus protecting the signal circuitry from overloading effects, and maintaining a constant output level.

AFC (automatic frequency control) – This is a technique whereby the receiver tuned frequency is automatically locked on to the optimal tuning point. This reduces the risk of tuning drift with temperature and humidity changes.

Algorithm – An orderly set of programmed instructions designed to perform a particular task. For example, tuning algorithms are often used in voltage synthesized tuning systems.

Bandwidth – The total range of frequencies occupied by a particular signal.

Baseband – A term used to describe the unprocessed or raw video frequencies (unde-emphasized and unclamped) plus the audio subcarriers.

De-emphasis – The reversal of pre-emphasis, a technique used to boost high frequencies prior to transmission. Since noise density increases with frequency, the subsequent de-emphasis reduces the signal level to normal and consequently attenuates the high frequency noise acquired during the transmission path.

Deviation – A measure of how much a carrier is deviated from its centre frequency by the modulating signal.

FM demodulator – A circuit which recreates the original signal from a frequency modulated carrier. This circuit is sometimes referred to as a discriminator.

IF (intermediate frequency) – A term used to describe the output frequency of signals from a down-conversion or mixer circuit (frequency changing circuit).

Local oscillator – A term used for a sinewave oscillator (sinusoidal signal generator) which is used in conjunction with a mixer stage.

MAC – Multiplexed analogue components. A TV system, to reduce cross-modulation effects and be compatible with future high definition TV developments.

Mixer – A circuit whose function is to generate sum and difference frequencies from an incoming RF signal and a local oscillator.

RF (radio frequency) – A term used to imply that the signal frequency is modulated onto a high frequency carrier.

uPc – An abbreviation for microprocessor or pre-programmed microcomputer chips. These are often used for system control and frequency synthesis tuning systems.

The tuner/demodulator

The satellite tuner demodulator is commonly manufactured as a single unit or 'can'. The down-converted range of frequencies (channels) are fed from the LNB via cable to the input of the tuner/demodulator can. This connection is normally via an F connector socket mounted directly on the can itself. Inside the tuner unit the following circuit blocks are frequently found.

1 Injection of d.c. LNB supply voltage.
2 d.c. isolation of the tuner input from 1.
3 An AGC controlled RF stage and filter.
4 A second down-conversion stage (2nd IF).
5 FM demodulator.
6 An AGC stage.
7 AN AFC stage.

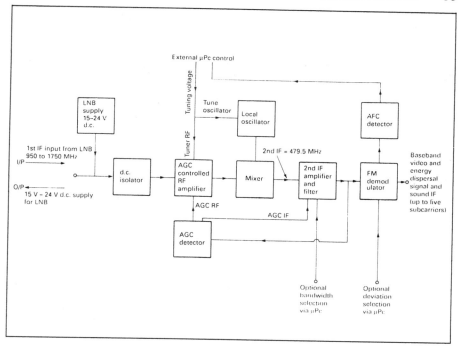

Figure 4.1 *Block schematic of a typical tuner/demodulator module*

Figure 4.1 shows a typical arrangement found in satellite tuner/ demodulator modules.

LNB supply voltage injection

The d.c. voltage requirement of a typical LNB unit is in the region of 15 to 24 V. This voltage, derived from the power supply of the receiver, is injected into the input cable to power the LNB. The RF input stage of the receiver must be protected from this voltage so a d.c. isolation circuit is included. D.C. isolation can be effectd by input capacitors or trans- formers. Some systems also have a voltage level shift method of switch- ing the V/H polarizer. This is achieved by sending, say, 13 V d.c. up the cable to switch the polarizer for vertical polarized signals or 17 V to switch the polarizer for horizontal polarized signals. This simple V/H switch method is encountered in many manufacturers' early Astra packages employing the 'Marconi' 1.8 dB LNB.

The AGC controlled RF stage

The incoming block of channels is applied to the input of the RF stage. Here, a degree of tuning often takes place where the required channel is roughly tuned and RF gain is applied. The gain of the circuit is controlled by a voltage derived from the 2nd IF output because strong signals will require less amplification or gain than weak ones. Tuning is normally controlled by a microcomputer chip or tuning processor whereby a control voltage is made to vary the bias applied to vari-cap (variable capacitance) diode circuits. However, the majority of the tuning and filtering is performed by the 2nd down-conversion and IF amplifier stages.

Local oscillator and mixer stages

The local oscillator output and the incoming RF signal are fed into a mixer stage where both sum and difference signals of the required channel are generated. Only the difference signals are utilized so the sum frequency band is filtered out by the IF amplifier stage. The frequency of the local oscillator is varied by a control voltage provided by a microcomputer or tuning processor. Whatever channel is selected, the mixing of the two frequencies translates the incoming signal to a fixed band of frequencies centred around a nominal 460 MHz but this is not standardized and can vary depending on the particular model of receiver. The output of the mixer stage is referred to as the second down-conversion or 2nd IF frequency.

2nd IF amplifier and filter

The purpose of the 2nd IF amplifier is to shape the signal to the required band pass characteristic and provide the majority of the signal gain. Only the selected channel's range of frequencies are allowed to pass through the IF filter stage. The IF filter bandpass characteristic can vary between 16 MHz and 36 MHz but is commonly found to be around 27 MHz. For example, Astra satellite receivers have the IF filter characteristic shown in Figure 4.2. Receivers designed to receive Eutelsat II series transmissions

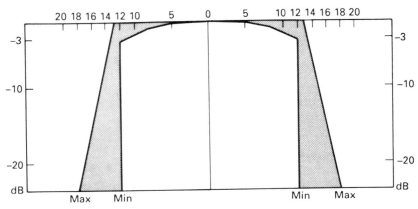

Figure 4.2   *IF filter characteristic for Astra receivers*

will need wider IF filter characteristics of 36 MHz. Overall, the IF amplifier stage can be considered as a channel band-pass filter with gain. In some high quality receivers it is possible to alter the bandwidth of the IF amplifier to suit transmissions from a wide range of satellites. This facility also has the advantage of reducing the noise content of signals during bad reception conditions by restricting the signal bandwidth to less than the normal value, although a loss of picture fidelity is the cost of the tradeoff. In the majority of designs, the 2nd IF amplifier is also AGC controlled in order to automatically boost weak signals relative to strong ones. The output of the second IF stage is used as the input to the AGC detector stage whose output is used to control the gain of the RF and IF stages.

The FM demodulator

The purpose of the FM demodulator is to reconstitute the original video band of frequencies and the accompanying audio subcarriers from the chosen channel bandwidth and strip off the carrier. The output from the FM demodulator is called the baseband signal. A broadband FM demodulator is quite complex and is often based on a piece of circuitry known as a phase locked loop (PLL). Figure 4.3 shows the basic operation of a phased locked loop demodulator. The frequency of a voltage controlled oscillator (VCO) is made to follow the incoming changes in frequency. The control voltage input to the VCO is also the demodulated signal output. The frequency output of the VCO, with zero control voltage is called the natural frequency and its value is chosen to be equal to the 2nd IF frequency.

FM demodulator operation

The signal from the VCO is compared with the incoming 2nd IF frequency. The phase detector generates an error signal which is related to the frequency or phase difference between the two inputs. The error

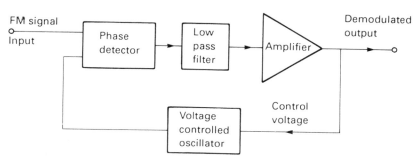

Figure 4.3 *Phase locked loop FM demodulator*

signal from the phase detector is low-pass filtered, amplified and used to control the frequency of the VCO. If the incoming frequency is sufficiently close to the frequency of the VCO then the feedback nature of the loop will cause the VCO to lock onto the incoming frequency. When in lock, any small phase errors detected are immediately corrected by the feedback loop so that the VCO, accurately and virtually instantaneously, tracks the deviations of the incoming signal. Providing the VCO is made to be sufficiently linear its control voltage is proportional to the required demodulated or baseband signal. The control voltage varies at a maximum rate equal to the maximum frequency of the modulated frequency. The low pass filter in the loop is thus set to this maximum frequency so that the effects of out of band interference and noise are suppressed. The principal advantage of phase locked loops over other forms of FM demodulation are:

1   It is easy to obtain a linear relationship between the incoming frequency deviations and the corresponding output voltages.
2   PLL circuits do not need any tuned circuits, which can be difficult to align.
3   PLL circuits exhibit better performance on signals affected by noise.

The output from the FM demodulator is the baseband signal which incorporates the video information, audio subcarriers and energy dispersal signal. The baseband signal has a typical bandwidth of 10 MHz.

Some up-market multi-satellite receivers incorporate selectable deviation values as well as bandwidths to match a wide range of transponder formats. These are usually controlled by microcomputer chips where the values can be stored and recalled from memory as part of the overall tuning process.

Energy dispersal signal

Under certain modulation conditions, frequency components in the FM spectrum can lead to interference with other users in the same frequency band. This is undesirable, so a 25 Hz triangular waveform, locked to the video signal field rate is produced, during uplink transmission, to cause energy dispersal. The corresponding carrier deviation of this signal varies from 600 kHz for D-MAC to 2 MHz for PAL.

Demodulator or receiver threshold

The object of good satellite receiver design, commensurate with economic considerations, is to incorporate an FM demodulator which has a linear characteristic between the carrier to noise ratio input and signal to noise ratio output, over the widest possible range. However, at some point the linear relationship begins to break down. The point where the

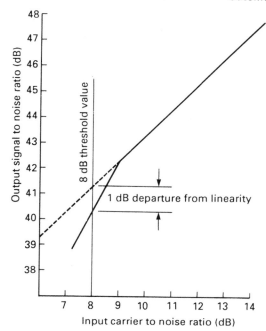

Figure 4.4 *Typical FM demodulator threshold performance*

deviation from linearity reaches 1 dB is the universally accepted point, known as the demodulator threshold. At, or near, this point sparklies or impulse noise begin to appear on the screen. At the time of writing, typical receiver threshold values are in the region of 8 dB, but expected improvements in threshold extension techniques in the 1990s will ulti-mately lead to even lower values and consequently antenna sizes as we shall see in Chapter 5. The concept of demodulator threshold is best understood by studying Figure 4.4; the demodulator input C/N ratio is plotted against the output S/N ratio. The straight line portion of the graph corresponds to the linear region of operation. At a C/N ratio of 8 dB the output linearity departs by 1 dB from the linear relationship, shown extrapolated by the dotted line. Thus the demodulator threshold repre-sented by this graph is 8 dB.

Automatic frequency control (AFC)

An output derived from the FM demodulator is fed to an AFC detector. The purpose of this circuit is to provide an error signal of the correct polarity to achieve any necessary correction voltages required to trim the tuned input stages. This is sometimes controlled indirectly by a tuning processor or microcomputer chip. Without this facility, a tendency to drift off tune may occur due to changes in temperature or humidity levels.

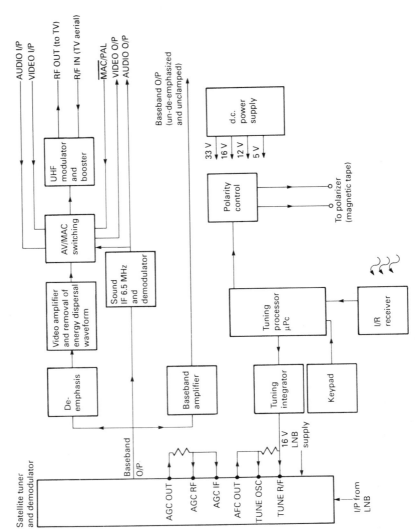

Figure 4.5 Block schematic of a basic satellite receiver

Baseband processing

The baseband signal output from the tuner/demodulator module is typically 250 mV peak to peak and contains the video information, energy dispersal and audio subcarriers. A block schematic of a no-frills satellite receiver is shown in Figure 4.5. The baseband output is split three ways to the video processing stage, sound demodulator stage, and external baseband stage.

External baseband signal

The raw output from the FM tuner/demodulator is boosted to 1 V p-p into a 75 ohm load by the baseband amplifier. This signal, under-emphasized and unclamped, is fed to external AV/MAC connectors, and is provided to enable the fitment of external decoders such as MAC. MAC decoders, D-MAC in particular, also require a baseband signal bandwidth of 25 Hz to 10.5 MHz. Later versions of receivers may incorporate MAC decoders internally.

Video processing

The raw baseband signal is first de-emphasized and fed into a video amplifier stage which not only makes good the losses incurred in de-emphasis but brings up the signal in level to 1 V p-p, the standardized composite video level. In some receivers the video de-emphasis can be switched between PAL or linear. Within this stage a clamping circuit removes the 25 Hz energy dispersal signal and a filter circuit removes all the audio subcarriers above the upper edge of the video band. The output of the video amplifier, called the baseband composite video signal, is fed to an AV/MAC switching stage which is explained later. Teletext signals are often transmitted in the vertical blanking period and up to fifteen lines of this period are commonly used. An oscilloscope trace of the baseband composite video signal is shown at Figure 4.6.

Sound processing

Again, the number and centre frequencies of sound subcarriers are not standardized. Furthermore, differing sound de-emphasis levels can be encountered, one is 62 µs and the other is known as the standard J17. Some receivers allow switching between the two. For purposes of simplification the following explanation will assume we have a dedicated Astra receiver; other satellite transmissions will have similar facilities but not necessarily using the same frequencies.

The baseband signal obtained from the Astra satellite is shown in Figure 4.7; the video band extends from zero to 5 MHz. A primary audio carrier centred on 6.5 MHz is provided for monophonic, single language

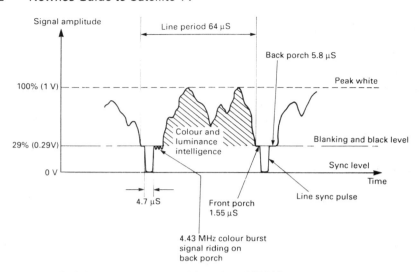

Figure 4.6   *Baseband composite video signal (PAL)*

transmissions and four separate subcarriers centred on 7.02, 7.20, 7.38 and 7.56 MHz are provided for stereo or multi-lingual transmissions. This later group of four sound carriers have smaller deviations and bandwidths.

In addition to the primary audio subcarrier, a stereo sound signal and two more audio channels can be transmitted using the four extra

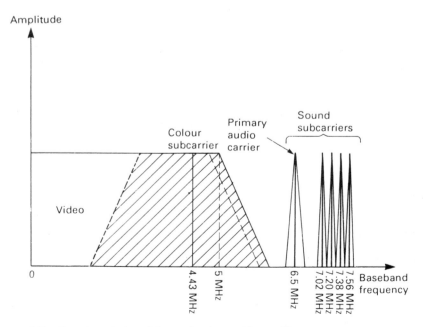

Figure 4.7   *Baseband signal from the Astra 1A satellite*

subcarriers. The extra two channels need not be related to the video service and may be radio transmissions, a second stereo language or two additional monophonic languages. Sometimes, all four channels can be utilized to transmit different languages in mono. This configuration is often found with multi-lingual commentaries on the sport channels. Some low cost receivers are totally monophonic and tend to rely on the primary audio subcarrier reception only and this is the simplest design outlined in Figure 4.6. However, if the receiver is designed to demodulate all four narrow bandwidth sound subcarriers (stereo and multi-lingual) then it will not need to demodulate the primary subcarrier since this always carries a monophonic duplicate of the corresponding stereo channel or language.

Specification of primary audio signal

Subcarrier frequency	6.5 MHz
Audio bandwidth	20 Hz–15 kHz
Deviation	plus or minus 85 kHz
Pre-emphasis time constant	50 μs
Modulated subcarrier bandwidth	180 kHz
Modulation index	0.26

Specification of additional narrow bandwidth subcarriers

Subcarrier frequencies	7.02, 7.20, 7.38 and 7.56 MHz
Audio bandwidth	20 Hz–15 kHz
Deviation	plus or minus 50 kHz
Pre-emphasis	Wegener Panda 1 system (adaptive pre-emphasis)
Modulated subcarrier bandwidth	130 kHz
Modulation index	0.15

Audio combinations used in Astra 1A transmissions

Audio channel	A	B	C	D
Subcarrier freq. (MHz)	7.02	7.20	7.38	7.56
Mode 1	Lang 1 (L)	Lang 1 (R)	Lang 2 (L)	Lang 2 (R)
Mode 2	Lang 1 (L)	Lang 1 (R)	Lang 2 (M)	Lang 3 (M)
Mode 3	Lang 1 (M)	Lang 2 (M)	Lang 3 (M)	Lang 4 (M)

where Lang = language, L = left audio channel, R = right audio channel and M = monophonic.

In order to obtain a high S/N ratio the four stereo/multi-lingual sound channels use the licensed Wegener Panda 1 noise reduction system.

AV/MAC switching

Most satellite receivers have the facility for connecting external decoders and de-scramblers. In the simplest case, all that is required is a means of routing composite video and audio signals to the UHF modulator from either internal circuitry or externally from, say, a MAC decoder. An externally generated switching voltage from the decoder is routed via the connector to control the switching. Remember that the external decoder input is obtained from the raw baseband signal.

Modulator/booster

The UHF modulator generates a UHF carrier signal typically at 607.25 MHz (channel 38). The carrier frequency is usually adjustable between channels 24 and 40 in case there is interference patterning with local TV stations or VCRs operating at or near this channel frequency. Both the composite video and audio signals are AM modulated onto the carrier. The modulator normally provides a loop-through facility so that a terrestrial TV aerial can be connected at the rear of the receiver. A certain amount of gain is added, to compensate for the losses incurred in combining the two signal sources. Terrestrial TV signals and the RF signal output from the modulator are combined into one common RF output socket at the back of the receiver. Without the loop-through facility a passive combiner would have to be used leading possibly to a decrease in signal level. The UHF modulator is provided for connection to older TV sets not having SCART/PERITEL sockets which provide for direct composite video and audio connection.

Power supplies

A range of power supply voltages are required in satellite receivers. A stabilized 33 V line is typically required to bias the vari-cap diodes in the tuner/demodulator module. A regulated 12 V supply is required for all the analogue circuitry such as sound and video processing circuits as well as the main power to the satellite tuner/demodulator module. A regulated 5 V supply is often needed for digital circuits, remote control receivers and display drivers. Supplies for the head unit polarizer and LNB are typically 12 and/or 15 V, and regulated.

Polarizer control

The selection of the required linear polarization sense, either vertical or horizontal, is performed by the polarity control circuit. This is a fairly complex piece of circuitry which maintains a constant current through a solid state magnetic polarizer embedded in the feedhorn. Polarization sense is critically determined by the accuracy of the current flowing through the polarizer windings. In order to ensure this current is constant over a wide range of outside operating temperatures, highly sensitive regulatory circuits need to be employed to compensate. The direction of current flow (typically 35 mA) determines whether vertical or horizontal polarization is selected and this is commonly stored and controlled by the tuning processor or system microcomputer chip. A variation on this principle is that the polarization sense is selected by passing either zero current or 70 mA through the windings. Some head units, designed for single satellite reception, employ simple V/H switching of 90° spaced dual probes built into the head unit. In these cases, a simple d.c. voltage level shift in the LNB feed is all that is required from the receiver to control the polarizer.

On some up-market receivers employing magnetic polarizers, it is possible to program and store optimum polarization adjustments for each channel. The reason being that the amount of wave twisting that is needed for each polarization sense is not only governed by the current through the polarizer but also, to a lesser extent, by the channel frequency of the signal. The facility to program in the relevant trim, by finely adjusting the current flowing in the polarizer windings, ensures spot-on polarization for all channels in the band. The major disadvantages with this are that the initial setting up of the channel tuning can be tedious and the extra wiring can lead to increased installation time. A maximum wave twisting range slightly in excess of 90° is often provided.

A few polarizers are three-wire mechanical devices and work by feeding voltage pulses to a servo motor which physically rotates a polarizer probe through 90°. The mark to space ratio of the pulses determines the amount of rotation. The 3 wire connections to a polarizer of this type are, +5 V line, ground, and a pulse line. Mechanical polarizers are not used much nowadays and the current trend leans more toward the use of the magnetic type in up-market models.

One of the main conclusions to draw from these possible polarizer/receiver variants is that extreme care must be exercised when putting together a system from different manufacturers' units. A sound knowledge of polarizer/receiver compatibility is necessary, otherwise costly and potentially embarrassing mistakes can be made.

Decoders and AV sockets

Most satellite receivers have some method of connecting de-scramblers or MAC decoders. In addition many have a method of direct connection of AV (audio/video) signals to a suitably equipped VCR or TV. This practice bypasses the UHF modulator section of the satellite receiver and will consequently lead to improved sound and picture quality. The vast majority of satellite receivers of European origin utilize either the 21 pin SCART/PERITEL type of socket, or the 15 pin subminiature 'D' type socket or sometimes both. Some models have one socket wired for direct AV to a VCR or TV and, in addition, another socket specifically for the connection of decoders. This latter socket is usually clearly labelled 'decoder only'. The reason is that the raw baseband signal, derived from the satellite tuner/demodulator, is required for input to decoders such as MAC, whereas ordinary VCR and TV sets require processed PAL composite video signals at a nominal 1 V p-p. Some low cost receivers dispense with this additional socket and use a single socket which can be used for either purpose. The provision of baseband or composite video is determined by a switching signal on a specific pin of the socket as explained later. Another method sometimes encountered is the provision of the baseband output on a non-standard or reserved pin, rarely used in AV connections to VCRs or TVs.

The standard SCART/PERITEL connector

The SCART/PERITEL connector, sometimes referred to as the Euroconnector, is a convenient 21 pin socket for the interconnection of various signals to/from domestic electronic equipment. The pin layout is shown in Figure 4.8. This type of wiring is the standard used for AV connection to VCRs and TVs and is often additionally used as a decoder interface connector on satellite receivers.

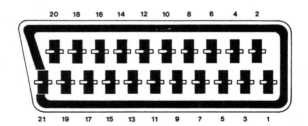

Figure 4.8 *SCART/PERITEL pin numbers (front view)*

Standard AV SCART/PERITEL pin connections:

PIN SIGNAL

    1 Audio output (right)
    2 Audio input (right)
    3 Audio output (right)
    4 Audio earth
    5 Blue earth (RGB)
    6 Audio input (left)

7 Blue video (RGB)
8 AV source switching voltage (see text)
9 Green earth (RGB)
10 Data line
11 Green video (RGB)
12 Data line
13 Red earth (RGB)
14 Data line earth
15 Red video (RGB)
16 Video blanking signal
17 Composite video earth
18 Video blanking signal earth
19 Composite video output
20 Composite video input
21 Overall shield earth

An extra SCART/PERITEL socket for external decoders

When a SCART/PERITEL socket is additionally fitted for the connection of external decoders the output available at pin 19 is the raw baseband signal and not the clamped and de-emphasized composite video as in the standard specification. Sockets of this type are normally labelled 'DECODER ONLY'. The source switching line on pin 8 is held high (+12 V) by the decoder to inform the satellite receiver to return, or switch in, audio and video signals from it. When this line is switched low (0 V, decoder switched off or disconnected) the receiver routes its own internally processed signals to the additional AV socket or UHF modulator. On most models pins 5 and 7 and pins 9 to 16 remain unused in the decoder socket, so these pins are normally linked through to the corresponding pins of the additional AV socket. This allows component RGB signals to be routed, from the decoder, directly to the TV or VCR. In this way the benefits of MAC decoded signals can be enjoyed providing the TV is a modern one which accepts RGB input and the MAC decoder derives the component RGB output.

A single SCART/PERITEL socket for AV or external decoder connection

Some satellite receivers have a single SCART socket that can be used for either connection to external decoders or AV direct connection to a VCR or TV. For AV mode, pin 8 is held high by the satellite receiver so that any connected VCR or TV is automatically switched to receive its internally processed signals. Thus de-emphasized and clamped composite video is available at pin 19 of the satellite receiver's SCART socket.

When an external decoder is connected, pin 8 must be pulled low by the decoder, or by human intervention, to enable the raw under-emphasized and unclamped baseband signal to be available at pin 19. When pin 8 is low, in these designs, the returned audio and video signals from the decoder are switched to the UHF modulator. Internally processed signals from the receiver are switched out thus are no longer available.

Another method used to utilize the same SCART socket for AV or external decoder connection is to direct the baseband output signal to a pin normally reserved for other uses. Sometimes pin 8 is not used as the switching voltage. In these and other receivers, it is important to check the manufacturer's instructions or consult the model's service manual before connecting decoders. However, for AV use this is not particularly important, since the majority of SCART to SCART connector cables are simply composite video and audio connected. That is to say, most of the pins remain unconnected.

An extra 'D' type socket for external decoder connection

Some models of Astra satellite receivers employ the 15 pin, subminiature, 'D' type socket for connection to external decoders. The pin layout is shown in Figure 4.9.

Pin connections to D type socket:

Pin	Signal	Details
1	Return audio input (left)	500–700 mV into 10 k load.
2	Return video input (PAL)	1 V p–p into 75 ohms.
3	Video switching voltage*	Switch receiver to return video from decoder if + 12 V applied.
4	Baseband output	Under-emphasized and unclamped video.
5	PAL video output (clamped)	1 V p–p into 75 ohms.
6	Return audio input (right)	500–700 mV into 10 k load.
7	Audio switching voltage*	Switch receiver to return audio from decoder if + 12 volts applied.
8	Earth	0 V.
9	Reserved	Future applications.
10	Reserved	Future applications.
11	Earth	0 V.
12	Audio output (left)	500–700 mV into 10 k load.
13	Audio output (right)	500–700 mV into 10 k load.
14	Reserved	Future applications.
15	Reserved	Future applications.

*Some receivers may have a single + 12 V line, switching both audio and video at the same time.

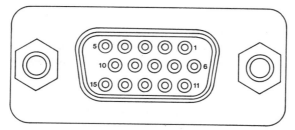

Figure 4.9 *Decoder 'D' type socket pin numbers (front view)*

D-MAC and UK satellite broadcasting

The complex details of the D-MAC system would warrant the space of a separate book so only a brief introduction follows. The D-MAC packet system has been adopted as the standard for the UK DBS service for the following reasons:

1 Low equipment cost and potentially rapid receiver sales in the initial stages.
2 Future-proof in that phased developments toward high definition TV (HDTV) can be pursued. This is not possible with the present PAL systems.
3 D-MAC transmission carries twice the data-handling capacity of D2-MAC, thus providing potentially more sound and data channels.

The alternative venture into 1125 line 60 Hz HDTV, developed by the Japanese, is far too costly in the initial stages to take off on a commercial basis in the UK. The launch and operation of the first BSB satellite provides the capability of improved picture quality on some modern TV sets in the first stages of development, leading eventually, in a number of stages, to full HDTV reception using alternative, wide screen aspect ratios.

Advantages of D-MAC over PAL

MAC systems have considerable advantages over composite video systems like PAL or SECAM and these are briefly outlined below:

1 The absence of cross-colour and cross-luminance effects ('the checked jacket effect').
2 Improved FM signal to noise ratio performance.
3 The combined carrier of digital and analogue components leads to the availability of high quality sound and data services.
4 Absence of subcarriers for sound and colour signals allows an increase in video bandwidth and consequently in picture quality.

5 Picture aspect ratio can be standard 4:3 or 16:9 for future wide screen and HDTV developments.
6 The flexibility of conditional access of receivers using over-air addressing removes the need for external decoder boxes.

The four phase D-MAC receiver development

The development of D-MAC over a period of time is intended to result in full HDTV, via satellite, by the turn of the century.

Phase 1 – The introduction of a stand alone satellite receiver which re-modulates the D-MAC signals onto a UHF carrier for RF insertion into a conventional TV. The D-MAC signals are thus converted into PAL compatible signals. The advantages of D-MAC will not be resolved using this system unless direct RGB outputs are provided for modern sets equipped with fully wired SCART sockets. However it gets DBS off the ground in an inexpensive way and the high quality sound channels can be output to a stereo hi-fi system or to modern stereo TVs.

Phase 2 – Satellite receiving circuitry built into an integrated dual standard MAC/PAL TV receiver. The advantage of D-MAC will now be realized along with high quality sound channels. This phase will start shortly after Phase 1.

Phase 3 – The first wide screen integrated receivers will start to appear. These will exhibit the advantages of D-MAC transmissions with a wide screen aspect ratio of 16:9. From the start of the DBS service some transmissions will be in 16:9 format and this will increase with time. The equipment produced in phases 1 and 2 will be able to resolve both 16:9 and 4:3 transmissions on a standard 4:3 aspect ratio receiver by displaying the appropriate part of the picture. Extended definition (EDTV) may be displayed on some of these sets by using up-conversion scanning techniques (e.g. 100 Hz field rate).

Phase 4 – The first full HDTV receivers will begin to appear. These will have 1250 line 50 Hz pictures in wide screen format using a digitally assisted HD-MAC transmission system. However, these transmissions will be downward compatible with earlier equipment and the public will be allowed to judge whether the extra expense of HDTV receivers is justified.

The phased escalation to HDTV during the 1990s is a welcome boost for the domestic electronics trade and it is up to all concerned to ensure that this form of broadcasting is successful. Future developments are likely to be the bread and butter of the trade for years to come. D-MAC transmission standards are not exclusively used for the UK DBS service, they are also being increasingly used on semi-DBS satellites such as Astra, along with its variant D2-MAC. Incidentally, D-MAC decoders are also capable of decoding D2-MAC signals.

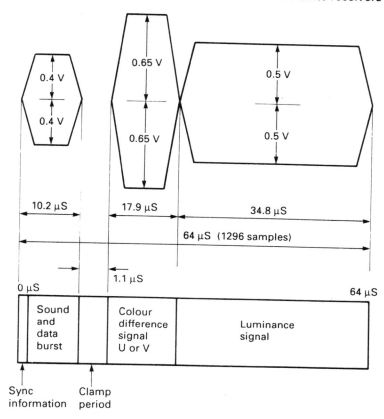

Figure 4.10 *Simplified D-MAC active line*

D-MAC transmission standards

D-MAC is an ingeniously flexible system, developed by IBA engineers, which transmits vision, sound and data within the allocated 27 MHz DBS bandwidth. The entire D-MAC baseband signal is frequency modulated using a deviation of 13.5 MHz/V. A triangular energy dispersal waveform with a deviation of 600 kHz is added to this. A carrier to noise ratio of about 12 dB allows vision quality in excess of grade 4 on the CCIR scale (see Chapter 5). The basic signal consists of a baseband time division multiplex of time-compressed colour and video signals preceded by a 20.25 Mbit/s duobinary burst signal which carries audio, data and digital synchronization information. Duobinary is a term given to a logic system which is more economical on bandwidth for a given data rate. Extreme positive and negative transitions are 'logic level 1' and intermediate values (zero volts) are 'logic level 0'. Compatibility with existing PAL receivers is achieved with a 625 line, 50 Hz field rate with 2:1 interface. The layout of one active line of a D-MAC signal is shown in Figure 4.10. A 10 μs duration duobinary burst of 206 bits is transmitted at the start of each 64 µs line. This relatively high data rate can encode up to eight high quality sound channels or a combination of sound, data and 'over air' conditional access signals. This digital information is arranged by the broadcaster into packets or subsections related to a particular service. For example, two stereo sound channels, teletext, and conditional access signals may be chosen for a particular service.

The colour difference bandwidth is 0 Hz to 2.75 MHz and the corresponding luminance bandwidth is 0 Hz to 5.75 MHz. However, colour difference signals are time compressed, prior to transmission, by a factor of 3:1 and the luminance signals by 3:2. The result of this is to increase the bandwidth by the same proportion thus increasing the overall video bandwidth to 8.75 MHz. Within the D-MAC decoder the analogue signal is sampled digitally at 20.25 MHz and stored in memory for reading out at the normal (non-time compressed) rate. The choice of 20.25 MHz for the digital sampling rate is related through the corresponding time compression ratios to the CCIR recommended studio sampling rates of 6.75 MHz for colour difference signals and 13.5 MHz for luminance signals. During the encoding process the $E'U_m$ colour difference signal is transmitted on odd numbered lines whilst the $E'V_m$ colour difference signal is transmitted on even lines. In the receiver the missing component is recovered by averaging the two signals on adjacent lines. A one line time delay is used in the luminance signal to compensate for this. The first six bit word of each sound/data burst signal contains line sync information. In addition line 625, a data only line, contains field sync information and other high priority data.

The sound/data burst multiplex

The 206 bit sound/data burst signal at the beginning of each active line (excluding line 625, which is the 1296 bit data only line) carry mainly sound and data. Most of the bits (198 per line) are subdivided into two groups of 99 bits per line. These are used over one frame period to construct two subframes of digital information as shown in Figure 4.11. Together these subframes convey 123 354 bits of information per television frame which corresponds to a data handling capacity of 3 083 850 bits/s. These subframes are further subdivided into discrete packets of 751 bits, each containing a 23 bit header for the receiver to select and identify those packets necessary for a particular broadcast while rejecting all others. The headers incorporate error protection codes so that erroneously received data can be detected and corrected.

Sound channels have built in flexibility, either high quality 15 kHz bandwidth (32 kHz sample rate) sound channels or 7 kHz bandwidth (16 kHz sample rate) commentary quality channels can be transmitted. High quality sound can be coded as 14 bit linear or compounded NICAM formats. The D-MAC system also offers a much higher teletext/data capacity than conventional PAL systems. However, these signals need to

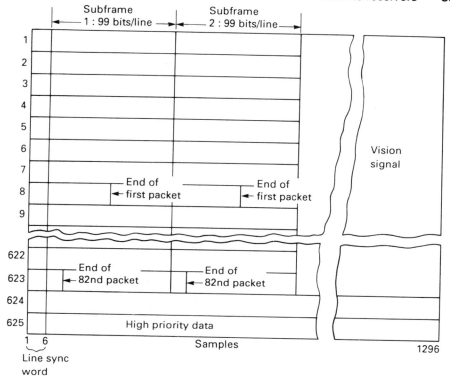

Figure 4.11 *Packet structure of sound/data multiplex*

be transcoded into the PAL vertical blanking period for decoding and display by a conventional teletext receiver. The D-MAC vertical flyback interval is reserved for future developments, such as HDTV, where control data, sent during the vertical flyback period, is to be used by specially adapted television receivers, to reconstruct a 1250 line picture. This technique is known as 'digitally assisted television' (DATV).

Receivers' data requirements

Since the D-MAC system is so flexible, certain signals and information need to be sent to the receiver in order that it can successfully process the correct picture information, data and sound channels. This information is sent as follows:

High priority data – This information is contained in line 625 of each frame and contains two basic types of information. Firstly, static information which does not change significantly from frame to frame, such as satellite identification, date, and time. Secondly, dynamic information which contains details of the complete multiplex structure of a satellite channel signals so that the receiver can gain access to its transmissions. Included in this portion are the digital frame synchronization signals.

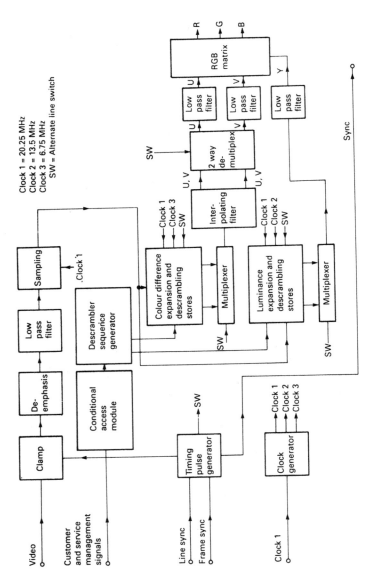

Figure 4.12 *Video processing in a D-MAC decoder*

Service identification channel – This medium priority information is assigned packets in the sound/data multiplex and is used to convey information about the channel services and transmission characteristics. This allows receivers to be automatically configured to decode the correct service components of the channel. This information is repeated every so often so that a receiver that has changed channels or has just been switched on can quickly acquire the selected services.

Interpretation blocks – This low priority information is used to specify the correct audio channels corresponding to a particular transmission and prepare the receiver for any forthcoming changes in the selected sound service. This information is contained within packets of the sound/data multiplex.

Scrambling

The D-MAC sound and vision signals can be conveniently divided into a number of discrete samples or packets. The vision components can be subdivided into 1 256 discrete time periods or samples per line, and blocks of these samples may be transmitted in any order. A technique known as 'double cut component rotation' is used to mix up the colour difference and luminance segments in a psuedorandom manner over each line period. The chosen positions from 256 equally spaced cut points vary from line to line thus rendering the picture unintelligible. Two 8 bit numbers, one for each waveform, are produced by a pseudorandom number generator to determine the cut points. Only if the receiver is made aware of these cut point sequences can it successfully reconstruct the signals, and this is done by generating an identical series of pseudorandom numbers in the receiver. If the receiver does not know the cut point sequence then the picture is said to be scrambled and the locking of such, with hidden keys, is known as encryption. The key signals to unlock this scrambling sequence clearly need to be sent to the receiver. For a non-subscription service this unlocking sequence is provided free to all receivers. For a subscription channel, the key information to unlock the sequence will only be sent to individual receivers on receipt of the appropriate payment. This concept is known as conditional access or over-air addressing of receivers. Due to a technique known as cross-fading the viewer will be unaware of any quality degradation due to the cutting actions used in the scrambling or descrambling process. The complexity of a D-MAC video decoder section can be appreciated from Figure 4.12, but thankfully the whole lot is buried within a handful of chips and a few discrete components.

Sound and data scrambling can be effected by juggling the relevant useful sound/data burst packets in a pseudorandom fashion. The reverse process in the receiver (descrambling) can also be controlled by conditional access techniques.

Multi-standard MAC decoders

International cooperation by a number of semiconductor manufacturers in Europe has resulted in the development of chip sets for use by TV set manufacturers to implement the full C-MAC, D2-MAC and D-MAC packet standards in their products. If satellite 1st IF processing along with PAL and SECAM decoders are also incorporated then we are well on the way to a universal TV set or 'Euro-telly' which will require only the addition of a suitable outdoor unit (or two!). The chip set can handle the full MAC picture format plus up to eight mono or four stereo sound channels and is fully compatible with current TV set architecture. A conditional access section handles the descrambling and decryption of sound, vision and teletext signals. Both single and double cut conditional access descrambling can be handled along with 'pay-per-view' flexibility. Programme entitlements can be addressed 'over-air' by the use of a keyboard. The chip set has a dual aspect ratio provision for HDTV and can handle linear or compounded sound signals with 1st and 2nd level error protection.

It appears that all the carping about the multitude of transmission standards adopted in Europe is a bit of a red herring since current technology has or will overcome the difficulties with the manufacture of multi-standard TV receivers. However, this has not been an easy task and the chip set designers deserve a pat on the back. A set of silicon chips which handle all the MAC standards adopted in Europe plus the different methods of descrambling and decrypting them is a monumental task! When we open up a satellite receiver revealing a handful of chips, it is tempting to say 'there's nowt in it', perhaps we should spare a thought to the work that has been done in the design and production.

5 The linked budget calculation

Introduction

This chapter is perhaps the most difficult to digest probably due to its high mathematical content. However, it is strongly recommended that you make an effort to understand the basic concepts even if you are predisposed to a little mathematical phobia. To lighten the burden, where necessary, refer back to the graphs and tables presented in Chapter 2, in this way trends can be visualized instantly without necessarily delving into mathematical formulae. To reduce the tedium of arithmetic, the chapter ends with a computer program written in a universal subset of BASIC intended to run on any machine. The Confederation of Aerial Industries and other bodies also recommend that this calculation be performed for each transponder so that a suitably sized antenna and appropriate noise figure LNB can be specified. The link calculation is indispensable for putting together a system designed from various manufacturers' components, either for your own use or for sale to the public as a package. On the other hand, single manufacturer's packages can be quickly evaluated and compared with their product specification.

The linked budget calculation

The performance of a satellite TVRO system is affected by a number of physical factors including:

1 Antenna pointing errors.
2 The LNB noise figure.
3 The antenna diameter.
4 Humidity/rainfall changes.
5 Attenuation of microwave signals on their way to earth.
6 Temperature variations.
7 The receiver threshold figure.
8 Satellite station keeping accuracy.
9 Wind distortion and movement of antenna.
10 Scattering of signals due to blockages (trees, buildings, birds, aircraft, etc.).

The linked budget calculation is formulated to help minimize some of the effects of these factors in a quantitative way by ensuring good potential pointing accuracy and an adequate, predictable margin of carrier to noise ratio over the demodulator threshold value of the receiver. This is generally agreed to be at least 2 dB for noise free reception during rain. It is commonplace, for domestic electronic technicians and aerial riggers to rely on tables, provided by others, to obtain the necessary pointing angles for fixed dish satellite reception. This is all very well for existing popular satellites, but what about future launches or requirements out of the ordinary? A betting shop's requirement or a business need may be provided for by some obscure satellite. It is far better to be equipped with the necessary tools to calculate the angles for any present or future satellite as the need arises and be in a position to put your own system together to meet any particular need. In order to target any satellite, the only information required is the position of the required satellite in the equatorial arc and the site latitude and longitude. All the necessary angles can be found quickly with any scientific calculator with trigonometrical functions. You do not need to understand the mathematical concepts to use mathematics as a tool. However, a common cause of confusion concerns the terminology used for certain functions. For example, arc tan, is a term often encountered. On most scientific calculators this function is termed $\tan^{-1}$. All such synonymous terms, relevant to this subject, are listed below. Press the calculator keys on the right of the equals sign to perform the functions on the left hand side.

$$\text{arc sin} = \sin^{-1}$$
$$\text{arc cos} = \cos^{-1}$$
$$\text{arc tan} = \tan^{-1}$$
$$\text{antilog} = 10^x$$

Example using the 10^x function.

$$F_{LNB} = 10^{(1.5/10)}$$

Divide 1.5 by 10 and press the equals button in the normal manner, then press the 10^x button on the calculator. This should give the approximate value of 1.41. Try it.

Making calculations easier

In view of the tedium involved in performing large numbers of calculations, a programmable scientific calculator or cheap home computer is a valuable asset. With programmable scientific calculators a program can be written instructing the calculator to perform various key strokes in a sequence. Many of these have continuous memory so the program will not be lost if the calculator is switched off. Input data, entered prior to running the program, is picked up from memory and operated on. The output data is then stored in memory for display on command. A cheap home computer equipped with BASIC is even better. Suitable programs for a variety of such machines are given later.

Effective isotropic radiated power (EIRP)

An isotropic radiator is defined as one which radiates uniformly in all directions. This is not obtainable in reality but is easy to visualize. By using a reflector an isotropic radiator can concentrate all its energy into a narrow beam which appears to some distant observer, at the other end of the beam, as an isotropic source of several magnitudes greater power output. Thus the term effective isotropic radiated power is used as a measure of signal strength that a satellite transmits to earth. EIRP is measured in dB per watt (dBW) and is highest at the beam centre. This value decreases linearly at distances away from the beam centre. The EIRP of any satellite can be obtained from the appropriate footprint map, as contours of equal magnitude. Modern satellites can shape their EIRP contours to a certain extent to fit the desired service area although the methods used need not concern us here. A typical value of EIRP for medium power semi-DBS satellites such as Astra 1A is 52 dBW. High power DBS satellites such as that operated by BSB have EIRP values in excess of 60 dBW.

Starting from scratch

As each equation of the linked budget calculation is introduced a real life practical example will be given on its use which will incorporate the results of previous calculations. We will evaluate a hypothetical Astra satellite receiver package to be installed in the Wirral district of Merseyside. The Astra 1A satellite is positioned at 19.2° east of south and each channel has a bandwidth of 26 MHz, a video deviation of 16 MHz/volt and video bandwidth of 5 MHz. From a local ordnance survey map, or its equivalent, the site longitude is found to be 3°W and the latitude 53.33°N. The magnetic variation from grid north is 5.5°W. True north is 1° east of grid north so the total magnetic variation is 6.5°W. We will need to add this to the calculated true azimuth bearing to arrive at a compass bearing.

Satellite position

Each satellite has a unique position, or orbital slot, over the equator at a height of approximately 36 000 km (22 300 miles). Their positions are specified by their longitudes at the equator. These are specified as either east or west of the Greenwich meridian (0° longitude). For example, both Astra 1A and 1B have a specified longitudinal position of 19.2° east of south. For any point in the service area, specified by its latitude and longitude, a unique antenna orientation is needed to capture its signals. To specify this orientation we need to find two components, the first is the elevation and the second is the azimuth.

Elevation (*EL*)

Elevation is the angle from the horizontal (tilt of dish) which targets the chosen satellite. In the northern hemisphere the elevation will be lower the further north the receiving site. The equation for calculating elevation is given by Equation 5.1.

$$EL = \text{Arc tan} \, [\,(\cos \, C - 0.151269) / \sin C\,] \qquad (5.1)$$

where C = Arc cos [cos (*LS* − *LR*)cos*B*]
    LS = Longitude of satellite
    LR = Longitude of receiving site
    B = Latitude of receiving site

The longitude difference $(LS - LR) = 19.2 - (-3) = 22.2°$ for Wirral, Merseyside. Note that longitudes west of the Greenwich meridian are taken as negative values. Conversely, longitudes east of Greenwich are taken as positive values when performing the subtraction. This saves having to visualize the globe when longitudes transgress the Greenwich meridian at 0°. The problem is the same when longitudes transgress 180°. For example, suppose a hypothetical satellite was at 160.8°W and the receiving site was at 177°E which is the analogue on the other side of the world. Evaluating $(LS - LR)$ with all positive values would give $160.8° - 177° = -16.2°$, clearly an error. Using the rule above we get $-160.8° - 177° = -337.8°$. A difference of $-337.8°$ in global terms is the same as 22.2°. Since the cosine of angles in both these quadrants are positive the cosine values of the angles are identical (0.9259).

Merseyside UK example:

    C = Arc cos [(0.9259)(0.5972)]
      = Arc cos (0.5529)
      = 56.43°

    EL = Arc tan [(0.5529 − 0.151269) / 0.8332]
      = Arc tan (0.4820)
    EL = 25.73°

Azimuth (*AZ*)

True azimuth (swing of dish) is the angle from true north that targets the chosen satellite. Compass bearings are normally measured in degrees[(°)] from 0° to 360°. North, east, south and west have bearings of 0°, 90°, 180° and 270° respectively. The satellite belt is targeted anywhere in the northern hemisphere by true azimuth bearings between 90° and 270°. Another way to specify true azimuth is in relation to due south in the northern hemisphere or due north in the southern hemisphere. The equation for calculating azimuth is given by Equation 5.2

$$AZ = \text{Arc tan} \left[\left(\tan (LS - LR) \right) / \sin B \right] \qquad (5.2)$$

Merseyside UK example:

$$AZ = \text{Arc tan} \ (0.4080 / 0.8021)$$
$$= \text{Arc tan} \ (0.5088)$$
$$AZ = 26.96° \text{ east of south}$$

True azimuth bearing $= 180° - 26.96° = 153.04°$

Adding in the magnetic variation correction we get:

compass bearing $= 153.04° + 6.5° = 159.54°$

Downlink path distance (*PD*)

Path distance is the distance between the receiving site and the chosen satellite. Clearly the further away from the equator the receiving site is located, the longer will be the path distance. The equation for path distance in kilometres is given at Equation 5.3

$$PD = (42\ 164 \sin C) / \cos EL \qquad (5.3)$$

Merseyside example:

$$PD = 42\ 164(0.8332 / 0.9008)$$
$$PD = 39\,000 \text{ km}$$

Wavelength (*W*)

It is customary for channel frequencies, rather than wavelengths, to be quoted in manufacturer's specifications for equipment. The conversion is very simple, divide the speed of light by the frequency and the result is the wavelength. All the link equations use wavelength rather than frequency. The equation to convert frequency to wavelength is given at Equation 5.4.

$$W = C / f \qquad (5.4)$$

where $C =$ the speed of light (3×10^8 m / s)
       $f =$ the channel frequency (Hz)

If we choose a channel whose frequency is 11.332 225 GHz and substitute this into Equation 5.4 we get:

Example:

$$W = 3 \times 10^8 / 11.332225 \times 10^9$$
$$W = 0.0265 \text{ m or } 2.65 \text{ cm}$$

Free space loss (A)

The free space loss or path loss expresses the attenuation of microwave signals on their way from the satellite to the receiving site. The path loss increases with frequency and is greatest at low elevation angles. Microwaves are reduced in energy and increasingly spread out on their earthward journey. Hence the difficulty in targeting only one specific European country by satellite. The microwaves radiated from the satellite antenna end up spilling over most of Europe. The equation used for calculating free space loss is given at Equation 5.5

$$A = 20 \ \log \ [(4\pi \times PD \times 1000) / W] \qquad (5.5)$$

where $\pi = 3.141 \ 59$

Merseyside example:

$$A = 20 \ \log \ [(4)(3.14 \ 159)(39 \ 000)(1000) / 0.0265]$$
$$= 20 \ \log \ (18 \ 499 \ 775 \ 090)$$
$$= 20 \times 10.2671$$
$$A = 205.34 \ \text{dB}$$

Antenna gain (G_a)

The higher the gain of the antenna then the better the satellite system will perform. A low gain antenna can sometimes be compensated by using a lower noise figure LNB. But below a certain minimum gain this tradeoff will cease to be useful. See Chapter 2 for a more detailed treatment of antenna gain.

$$G_a = 10 \ \log \frac{(\pi \times D)^2 \times P}{100 \times W^2} \qquad (5.6)$$

where $\pi = 3.141 \ 59$
$D =$ the diameter of the antenna
$P =$ the efficiency
$W =$ wavelength of the received signal.

Example:

The hypothetical system has an antenna diameter of 0.62 m, at its widest point, and has an efficiency of 67 per cent; from this we can now calculate the antenna gain (G_a) using Equation 5.6

$$G_a = 10 \log (254.19/0.0703)$$
$$= 10 \log (3615.8)$$
$$G_a = 35.58 \text{ dBi}$$

Noise factor (*F*)

The noise factor and noise figure of a LNB are equivalent, the noise factor is simply:

$$\text{Noise factor } (F) = \frac{\text{ideal or best possible } S/N}{\text{actual output } S/N}$$

The result is always > 1. However, the noise figure NF_{LNB} is traditionally expressed in decibel notation by using the expression, 10 log *F* which is always greater than zero. For our purposes we require the 'non decibelized' value which by convention is called the noise factor. Equation 5.7 involves the reversal of decibel notation.

$$F_{LNB} = 10^{(NF/10)} \tag{5.7}$$

where NF = the noise figure (dB)

Example:

The hypothetical Astra system LNB has a noise figure of 1.5 dB. The LNB noise figure, or any noise figure, can be converted to its equivalent noise factor (*F*) using Equation 5.7.

$$F_{LNB} = 10^{(1.5/10)}$$
$$= 10^{(0.15)}$$
$$F_{LNB} = 1.41$$

Noise temperature (*T*)

The LNB noise factor, or any noise factor, can be converted to its equivalent noise temperature at an average ambient temperature of 290°K using Equation 5.8

$$T_{LNB} = 290 \ (F-1) \tag{5.8}$$

Example:

$$T_{LNB} = 290(1.41 - 1)$$
$$T_{LNB} = 118.9°K$$

Total noise temperature (*T*$_{TOT}$)

Since the satellite signals are so very weak by the time they are received on earth, reception is marred by noise contributions from various sources. The value for T_{ANT} depends on the elevation angle of the dish. At high elevations, nearing the vertical, the majority of noise is sky noise. At lower elevation angles, nearing the horizontal, there is a large contribution from ground noise. The warm earth has an inherent noise temperature which is picked up by the antenna through its side lobes, the amount depending on the side lobe pattern itself. The total noise temperature, T_{TOT} is given by Equation 5.9

$$T_{TOT} = T_{LNB} + T_{ANT} \tag{5.9}$$

Example:

The antenna noise temperature T_{ANT} of our hypothetical Astra system is given in the manufacturer's specification as 95°K for UK latitudes.

$$T_{TOT} = 118.9 + 95 = 213.9°K$$

Noise bandwidth (*NB*)

Finally, on the subject of noise, we need to calculate the noise bandwidth. This is simply the RF channel bandwidth (26 MHz for Astra) converted to decibel notation. The relevant equation is Equation 5.10

$$NB = 10 \log (BW) \tag{5.10}$$

where $BW =$ the bandwidth of the signal

Example:

$$NB = 10 \log (26 \times 10^6)$$
$$= 74.15 \text{ dBHz}$$

Figure of merit (*G/T*)

The figure of merit is an overall measure of the performance of the antenna and LNB combination and the higher this value is, the better the system will perform. *G/T* is basically the ratio of antenna gain and total system noise. Other than the EIRP level, this is the figure which has the greatest effect on the final *C/N* ratio. All other contributory factors to *C/N* for any particular receiving site are relatively constant, as we will see later.

The figure of merit (*G/T*) is given by Equation 5.11

$$G/T = 10 \log \frac{10^{(Ga/10)}}{T_{TOT}} \tag{5.11}$$

Example:

$$G/T = 10 \log (3614.1 / 213.9)$$
$$= 10 \log (16.90)$$
$$G/T = 12.28 \text{ dB/°K}$$

Carrier to noise ratio (*C/N*)

An important parameter by which a satellite system performance is judged is the carrier to noise ratio, *C/N*. This value and the subsequently derived S/N_w value, transposed to the CCIR 5-point scale, is used to estimate the satellite system's overall level of performance. The carrier to noise ratio can be calculated from Equation 5.12

$$C/N = EIRP + G/T - BC - NB - A \qquad (5.12)$$

where *EIRP* = Effective isotropic radiated power
      G/T = Figure of merit
      BC = Boltzman's constant derivative (− 228.6 dBW/HzK)
      NB = Noise bandwith
      A = Free space loss

Example:

$$C/N = 52 + 12.28 - (-228.6) - 74.15 - 205.3$$
$$C/N = 13.43 \text{ dB}$$

The CCIR 5-point scale of impairment

C/N results are converted to S/N_w for matching up to the CCIR impairment scale which is given in Table 5.1. The weighted *S/N* values given are approximate due to the subjective nature of the scale and a compromise made between PAL and MAC signals. It is said that MAC broadcasts, all else being equal, are about a quarter grade better in performance than PAL. The use of 'threshold extension techniques' can alter *S/N* values to a certain degree, particularly around the grade 3 area, but the overall aim of system design is to achieve greater than 4 (*S/N* > 42 dB) on the scale.

Table 5.1 *The CCIR 5-point scale*

Quality	Grade	Impairment	S/N_w
Excellent	5	Imperceptible	> 50 dB
Good	4	Perceptible but not annoying	> 42 dB
Fair	3	Slightly annoying	> 36 dB
Poor	2	Annoying	–
Bad	1	Very annoying	–

Unweighted signal to noise ratio (S/N_{uw})

The unweighted signal to noise ratio (S/N_{uw}) is given by Equation 5.13,

$$S/N_{UW} = C/N + FMI + PE \qquad (5.13)$$

where FMI = FM improvement
$\qquad PE$ = Pre-emphasis improvement

The pre-emphasis improvement is applied to the transmitted signal and is typically around 2 dB in value. Since the noise power density of a receiver demodulator output increases with frequency, high frequencies are boosted or pre-emphasized prior to transmission. When the signal is subsequently demodulated the signal and its acquired noise content is de-emphasized or reduced by an equal amount. The overall effect is to reduce the noise component.

Weighted signal to noise ratio (S/N_w)

An additional factor called the weighting factor is added to give the weighted S/N ratio (Equation 5.14). This weighting factor, WF, is derived because of the difference between the calculated value of noise and the viewers' varying perception of differing spectra noise accompanying the video signal.

$$S/N_w = S/N + WF \qquad (5.14)$$

The weighting factor is a value derived from the particular signal type being transmitted. For example PAL-I signals have a CCIR weighting factor of 11 dB whereas MAC signals have a figure of 13 dB. Therefore it is to be expected that MAC transmissions will generally achieve better picture and sound quality than PAL using the same bandwidth. The S/W_W is the parameter used for matching up to the CCIR 5-point scale.

FM improvement (FMI)

The so called FM improvement (FMI) can be calculated from a knowledge of the modulating system and the RF and video bandwidths. It can be calculated using Equation 5.15

$$FMI = 10 \log \left[1.5(f/f_v)(B/f_v) \right] \qquad (5.15)$$

where f = video deviation
$\qquad f_v$ = highest video frequency
$\qquad B$ = RF bandwidth of the signal

From the equation we see that FMI depends on three parameters.

Highest video frequency (f)

The bandwidth of video signals varies according to the particular TV system adopted. For the UK terrestrial PAL system it is 5.5 MHz.

The range of frequencies extend from near 0 Hz, steady 'blank' raster, to 5.5 MHz, finest detail. Therefore the video bandwidth of the signal is 5.5 MHz. Some European PAL systems have a maximum value of 5 MHz and this is the value specified for the Astra 1A satellite. American NTSC is 4.2 MHz and the French SECAM system has a video bandwidth of 10 MHz. Reducing the video frequency range results in higher *FMI* values.

Deviation (f_v)

With frequency modulation, the instantaneous frequency of the modulated signal is varied in response to the instantaneous voltage value of the message signal. This modulation method produces an infinite number of frequency components as sidebands. However, the amplitude of these components decrease with the distance from the carrier frequency. For practical purposes, only a limited number of these components need be sent without affecting perceived picture quality. Bandlimiting these smaller components produces very little distortion and a minimum bandwidth, somewhat larger than the maximum deviation is normally sufficient. The maximum frequency deviation of the modulated signal, f_v, is the frequency difference between the maximum modulated frequency and the unmodulated frequency and corresponds to the maximum and minimum amplitude of the message signal respectively. The ratio of deviation and highest message frequency is often called the *frequency modulation index*. This depends on the sensitivity of the modulator and increasing this has the effect of spreading out the signal spectrum. The video deviation used in satellite transmissions is not standardized and can be anywhere between 13.5 and 28 MHz/volt. For example, the Astra 1A satellite specifies its channels as having a video deviation of 16 MHz/volt. Assuming a typical value of 1 volt peak to peak from sync level to peak white this gives a deviation value of 16 MHz. With D-MAC the complete baseband signal is frequency modulated with a deviation of 13.5 MHz/volt. Increasing the deviation of the transmitted signal results in a higher FMI value.

RF bandwidth (B)

The RF bandwidth, (B), of a microwave satellite signal is relatively large compared with its terrestrial AM counterpart and is normally in the range 15 MHz to 36 MHz. For medium power and DBS satellites, a transponder bandwidth of around 27 MHz is commonly used although the Eutelsat II series transponders, for example, have bandwidths of 36 and 72 MHz. With the latter it is possible to transmit two channels using the same transponder (half transponder format). The frequency spectrum of an FM modulated signal is infinite (produces an infinite range of sideband frequency components) therefore an infinite bandwidth would be needed to transmit it. Clearly, some form of compromise or bandlimiting is necessary in practice which must be related to the deviation value used. From subjective tests it has been found that picture quality derived from 27 MHz bandwidth signals are indistinguishable from those of 36 MHz or more and that bandwidths as low as 16 MHz produce reasonable picture quality. Reduction of bandwidth leads to a distortion of video fidelity accompanied by a reduction in noise. The tradeoff with wide bandwidths is a correspondingly lower number of channels that can be accommodated by the satellite over a given frequency range. However, this is not such a problem with high power DBS satellites since the number of channels are more restricted by their transponder energy requirements than bandwidth considerations. Increasing the bandwidth of the transmitted signal increases the *FMI* value thus a particular level of 'clear sky' performance can be obtained using a lower *C/N* ratio. This is why the Eutelsat II series of satellites, having wideband transponders of 36 MHz, can obtain greater than Grade 4 on the CCIR impairment scale with a lower *C/N* ratio than that of Astra systems.

To finish the calculation for our hypothetical Astra system we get:

$$FMI = 10 \log [1.5 \, (16/5)^2 \, (26/5)]$$
$$= 10 \log (79.87)$$
$$= 19.02 \text{ dB.}$$

$$S/N_{uw} = 13.43 + 19.02 + 2.0$$
$$= 34.45 \text{ dB}$$

$$S/N_W = 37.56 + 11.0$$
$$= 45.45 \text{ dB}$$

The S/N_w value when compared to the CCIR 5-point scale translates to greater than Grade 4 which is the overall aim.

Worst case calculation

It is often worthwhile to perform a calculation assuming the worst case, such as an out of spec LNB noise figure or a reduction in EIRP level at the fringe of the central service area. For our example we will assume that for some hypothetical reason the EIRP level has reduced by 2 dB and the particular LNB supplied has a noise figure of 1.7 dB instead of the quoted 1.5 dB. By repeating the linked budget calculation we find the *C/N* has reduced to 11.01 dB and the S/N_w has reduced to 43.03 dB. This still exceeds Grade 4 on the CCIR 5-point scale so our hypothetical system would operate satisfactorily over a relatively wide geographical area. A system installed on a sunny clear day may provide perfectly acceptable picture quality but during heavy rain, FM noise ('sparklies') may appear in varying degrees.

Rain attenuation and the importance of *C/N*

The figures calculated above assume a perfectly clear day with no precipitation. When rain, snow or fog are about the microwave signals are absorbed and scattered and can reduce the *C/N* value. Furthermore rain has an average noise temperature of 290°K which is considerably higher than that of clear sky. A fixed margin may be added to the *C/N* figure to account for average rainfall over a particular country or continent. But we must still expect heavy localized rainfall to occasionally attenuate signals to such a level that the *C/N* ratio is briefly below demodulator threshold and sparklies appear. The reduction in *C/N* may be sufficient, in a really heavy localized thunderstorm, to completely wipe out the picture and sound for a brief period. Since rainfall is very difficult to predict it does create a problem for system designers. Much work has been done by engineers to quantify the effects of rain on microwave signals, and one of the more general results from this work is a relationship between the elevation angle of the antenna and attenuation linked to average rainfall values for various zones of the world. Figure 5.1 shows the order of results for attenuation (11 / 12 GHz) v elevation angle, based on long-term average rainfall figures for Europe. The attenuation values correspond to rainfall figures not likely to be exceeded during more than 1 per cent of the worst month or 0.25 per cent of the time.

The minimum generally accepted *C/N* margin for a satellite TVRO system operating in Europe is 2 dB. Thus for a system to meet this requirement it must produce a *C/N* ratio of at least 2 dB above the

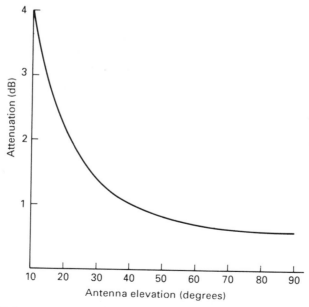

Figure 5.1   *Rain attenuation (11/12 GHz)*

receiver's demodulator threshold. However, the Astra operators recommend a 3 dB margin. They recommend that the receiver's demodulator threshold should be less than 9 dB *C/N*, and 'clear sky' reception of greater than 12 dB *C/N*. The vast majority of satellite receivers have a demodulator threshold of about 8 dB at the time of writing, therefore the *C/N* ratio to be aimed for must be at least 10 dB and preferably 11 dB. For even more resilience to occasional brief rain fades, a higher link margin could be engineered, but eventually the law of diminishing returns rears its head. Systems operating at, or near to, the receiver's demodulator threshold are likely to be plagued by sparklies during rain and inherit poor signal availability. Our worked example gave a *C/N* value of about 13.5 dB, 4.5 dB above receiver demodulator threshold, therefore we can expect a good tolerance to rain attenuation for most of the time. However, there will still be brief interruptions to the service at certain times and places, particularly at the fringes of the footprint area.

Other losses

Other allowances can be taken into account when establishing a link margin such as antenna pointing errors, typically 0.3 dB, and waveguide losses, 0.3 dB approx. These values can either be deducted from *C/N* or added to the link margin.

Deducing antenna size

When putting together a system from component parts, other than dustbin lids and Fray Bentos pie tins, it is necessary to find a reasonable starting point for antenna size! This can be done by working backwards on the linked budget equation. Start by assuming a receiver threshold value of about 8 dB and that the receiving site is Aberdeen, Scotland. The satellite we require to be targeted is Astra 1A which has at the receiving site, a worst case EIRP value of 49 dBW. Say we have a receiver with a demodulator threshold of 8 dB and we want a *C/N* link margin of 3 dB to allow for rain fade and other losses. Therefore, we want a *C/N* figure of 8 dB + 3 dB = 11 dB. By rearranging Equation 5.12 for *G/T* we arrive at Equation 5.16

$$G/T = C/N - EIRP + BC + NB + A \qquad (5.16)$$

Calculating in the usual manner we need the following results from the link equations.

Elevation = 22.33°
True azimuth = 155.10°
Path distance = 39 325.71 km
Free space loss = 205.35 dB
Noise bandwidth at 26 MHz = 74.15 dBHz
Wavelength (11.33 GHz channel frequency) = 0.0265 m

Substituting into Equation 5.16

$G/T = 11 - 49 + (-228.6) + 74.15 + 205.35$

$\qquad = 12.90$ dB

The antenna gain (G_a) can be expressed in terms of G/T by rearranging Equation 5.11. The resulting expression is given in Equation 5.17

$$G_a = 10 \log (10^{(G/T/10)} \times T_{TOT}) \qquad (5.17)$$

We will assume a total noise temperature in the region of 240°K a reasonable figure that can easily be achieved.

$G_a = 10 \log [(19.50)(240)]$

$\qquad = 36.70$ dBi

Assuming an antenna efficiency of 60 per cent we can now calculate the diameter by rearranging Equation 5.6 for diameter. The resulting equation is given at Equation 5.18

$$D = \{ [W^2(100)10^{(G_a/10)}] / P \}^{0.5} / \pi \qquad (5.18)$$

Where $\pi = 3.141\,59$

$D = \{ [(0.0265)^2(100)10^{(36.70/10)}] / 60 \}^{0.5} / 3.141\,59$

$\qquad = (328.46 / 60)^{0.5} / 3.141\,59$

$\qquad = 0.74$ m or 74 cm

Therefore to receive all sixteen channels from Astra 1A with a 3 dB link margin we would need at least a 74 cm antenna of 60 per cent efficiency with a gain of 36.70 dBi at 11.33 GHz. In fact the Astra operators recommend a 75 cm dish size for this area, so the calculations do hold in practice.

EIRP level v antenna diameter

Using the foregoing equations a table can be constructed showing the relationship between *EIRP* level and recommended minimum antenna diameter for a range of *C/N* values. Such a computer generated version is given in Table 5.2. The *C/N* values chosen consist of average receiver threshold at 8 dB and then further increments of 3 dB giving 11 dB, 14 dB and 17 dB. A typical value for most domestic Astra packages is 11 dB. Other uses such as SMATV would require the higher figures. As with all tables and graphs of this type, certain assumptions need to be made, so their accuracy cannot be taken too literally. However, they do give a general indication of antenna size requirements to receive any present or future satellite service. The main trends that can be deduced from Table 5.2 and the corresponding graph (Figure 5.2) is that the antenna size increases with *C/N* value but decreases with *EIRP* level. In compiling the table, the following worst case assumptions are made:

Table 5.2   *EIRP level v antenna diameter for various C/N ratios*

Based on following fixed values:

Free space loss = 205.7 dB
Antenna efficiency = 60 per cent
Total noise temperature = 240° K
Frequency = 11 GHz
Bandwidth = 27 MHz

	Dish diameter (metres)			
EIRP level (dBW)	C/N = 8 dB	C/N = 11 dB	C/N = 14 dB	C/N = 17 dB
30.00	5.13	7.25	10.24	14.46
31.00	4.57	6.46	9.13	12.89
32.00	4.08	5.76	8.13	11.49
33.00	3.63	5.13	7.25	10.24
34.00	3.24	4.57	6.46	9.13
35.00	2.89	4.08	5.76	8.13
36.00	2.57	3.63	5.13	7.25
37.00	2.29	3.24	4.57	6.46
38.00	2.04	2.89	4.08	5.76
39.00	1.82	2.57	3.63	5.13
40.00	1.62	2.29	3.24	4.57
41.00	1.45	2.04	2.89	4.08
42.00	1.29	1.82	2.57	3.63
43.00	1.15	1.62	2.29	3.24
44.00	1.02	1.45	2.04	2.89
45.00	0.91	1.29	1.82	2.57
46.00	0.81	1.15	1.62	2.29
47.00	0.72	1.02	1.45	2.04
48.00	0.65	0.91	1.29	1.82
49.00	0.58	0.81	1.15	1.62
50.00	0.51	0.72	1.02	1.45
51.00	0.46	0.65	0.91	1.29
52.00	0.41	0.58	0.81	1.15
53.00	0.36	0.51	0.72	1.02
54.00	0.32	0.46	0.65	0.91
55.00	0.29	0.41	0.58	0.81
56.00	0.26	0.36	0.51	0.72
57.00	0.23	0.32	0.46	0.65
58.00	0.20	0.29	0.41	0.58
59.00	0.18	0.26	0.36	0.51
60.00	0.16	0.23	0.32	0.46
61.00	0.14	0.20	0.29	0.41

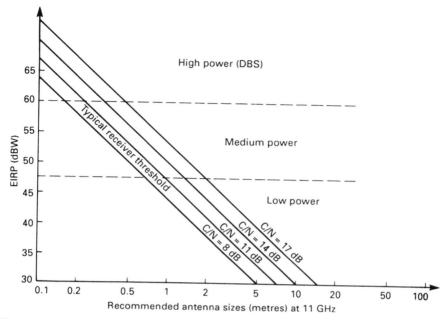

Figure 5.2 *EIRP level v antenna diameter for various C/N values*

1 The free space loss is assumed to be 205.7 dB worst case.
2 The frequency chosen is 11 GHz; this is toward the lower end of the allocated European fixed satellite service, again worst case.
3 Total noise temperature is assumed 240°K, this is rather higher than the majority of systems inherit.
4 Antenna efficiency is taken as 60 per cent, an easily obtainable figure these days.
5 Finally, the signal bandwidth is assumed 27 MHz.

Computer programs to perform linked budget calculations

Since the above linked budget calculation is so awesome, and long-winded to perform by hand, computerization seems the logical approach for the professional installation technician. This would also alleviate the need to acquire *AZ/EL* tables for each satellite in the geo-arc. Using a computer program and altering particular parameters is a fast way of learning the intricate details of satellite reception techniques and cannot be too strongly recommended. Simple home computers supporting the BASIC language can be bought new or secondhand very cheaply nowadays. You may have one already, stored under the stairs with the cables wrapped round it. The cost is very low compared with the other tools and equipment necessary for satellite TVRO installation work.

Program 5.1   Linked budget calculation (Universal BASIC version)

```
>LIST
   10REM********************************
   20REM*                              *
   30REM*    LINKED BUDGET CALCULATOR  *
   40REM*    (UNIVERSAL BASIC SUBSET)  *
   50REM*         DJ STEPHENSON        *
   60REM*                              *
   70REM********************************
   80GOSUB 230
   90GOSUB 1460
  100GOSUB 340
  110IF K$="Y" THEN GOSUB 450
  120GOSUB 700
  130IF EL<0 THEN PRINT"SATELLITE BELOW
HORIZON":GOTO 180
  140IF K$="Y" THEN GOSUB 870
  150GOSUB 1020
  160IF K$="Y" THEN GOSUB 1290
  170GOSUB 1460
  180PRINT"REPEAT PROGRAM (Y/N)";:GOSUB
1720
  190IF K$="Y" THEN 80
  200END
  210
  220REM INITIALISATION SUBROUTINE
  230P=3.14159265
  240GOSUB 1460:PRINT"LINKED BUDGET CALC
ULATOR"
  250PRINT"by DJ STEPHENSON":GOSUB 1460
  260PRINT"REQUIRE FULL LINK CALCULATION
 (Y/N)";:GOSUB 1720:PRINT
  270PRINT"INPUT FORMAT : ALL VALUES +VE
 EXCEPT"
  280PRINT"LONGITUDES WEST -VE"
  290PRINT"SOUTHERN HEMISPHERE LATITUDES
 -VE"
  300PRINT"MAGNETIC VARIATION WEST -VE"
  310RETURN
  320
  330REM INPUTA SUBROUTINE
  340PRINT"ENTER LONGITUDE OF SATELLITE
(DEG)"
  350LO=-180:HI=180:GOSUB 1620:LS=A
  360PRINT"ENTER LONGITUDE OF SITE (DEG)
"
  370GOSUB 1620:LR=A
  380PRINT"ENTER LATITUDE OF SITE (DEG)"
  390LO=-90:HI=90:GOSUB 1620:SL=A
  400PRINT"ENTER LOCAL MAGNETIC VARIATIO
N (DEG)"
  410GOSUB 1620:V=A
  420RETURN
  430
  440REM INPUTB SUBROUTINE
  450PRINT"ENTER CHANNEL FREQUENCY (GHZ)
"
  460LO=10:HI=14:GOSUB 1620:CF=A
```

```
470PRINT"ENTER ANTENNA DIAMETER (METRE
S)"
480LO=0.2:HI=5:GOSUB 1620:DI=A
490PRINT"ENTER ANTENNA EFFICIENTCY (%)
"
500LO=10:HI=100:GOSUB 1620:PP=A
510PRINT"ENTER ANTENNA NOISE TEMPERATU
RE (K)"
520LO=1:HI=200:GOSUB 1620:TA=A
530PRINT"ENTER LNB NOISE FIGURE (DB)"
540LO=0.5:HI=3:GOSUB 1620:NF=A
550PRINT"ENTER EIRP FIGURE (DBW)"
560LO=1:HI=100:GOSUB 1620:EI=A
570PRINT"BANDWIDTH OF SIGNAL (MHZ)"
580LO=5:HI=100:GOSUB 1620:BW=A
590PRINT"ENTER HIGHEST VIDEO FREQUENCY
(MHZ)"
600LO=3:HI=20:GOSUB 1620:VF=A
610PRINT"ENTER DEVIATION (MHZ)"
620LO=3:HI=100:GOSUB 1620:DV=A
630PRINT"ENTER PRE-EMPHASIS IMPROVEMEN
T (DB)"
640LO=1:HI=10:GOSUB 1620:PE=A
650PRINT"ENTER WEIGHTING FACTOR (DB)"
660LO=1:HI=50:GOSUB 1620:WF=A
670RETURN
680
690REM CALCA SUBROUTINE
700A=LS-LR:SN=SGN(A):A=ABS(A)
710DG=A:GOSUB 1500:A=R
720DG=SL:GOSUB 1500:B=R
730DG=V:GOSUB 1500:V=R
740X=COS(A)*COS(B):GOSUB 1580:C=AC
750EL=ATN((COS(C)-0.151269)/SIN(C))
760IF EL<0 THEN 840
770AZ=ATN(TAN(A)/SIN(B))
780AZ=P-SN*AZ
790CB=AZ-V
800IF SL<0 THEN AZ=AZ-P:CB=CB-P
810IF CB<0 THEN CB=CB+2*P
820IF AZ<0 THEN AZ=AZ+2*P
830PD=(42164*SIN(C))/COS(EL)
840RETURN
850
860REM CALCB SUBROUTINE
870W=3*10^8/(CF*10^9)
880FS=20*LOG(4*P*PD*1000/W)
890GA=10*LOG((((P*DI)^2)*PP)/((W^2)*10
0))
900FL=10^(NF/10)
910TL=(FL-1)*290
920TT=TA+TL
930GT=10*LOG((10^(GA/10))/TT)
940NB=10*LOG(BW*10^6)
950CN=EI+GT+228.6-NB-FS
960FI=10*LOG(1.5*((DV/VF)^2)*(BW/VF))
970SU=CN+FI+PE
980SW=SU+WF
990RETURN
1000
```

```
1010REM OUTPUTA SUBROUTINE
1020SL$=STR$(ABS(SL)):LS$=STR$(ABS(LS))
:LR$=STR$(ABS(LR))
1030R=V:GOSUB 1540:N=DG:GOSUB 1680:V=M
1040V$=STR$(ABS(V))
1050IF SL>0 THEN SL$=SL$+"N"
1060IF SL<0 THEN SL$=SL$+"S"
1070IF LS>0 THEN LS$=LS$+"E"
1080IF LS<0 THEN LS$=LS$+"W"
1090IF LR>0 THEN LR$=LR$+"E"
1100IF LR<0 THEN LR$=LR$+"W"
1110IF V>0 THEN V$=V$+"E"
1120IF V<0 THEN V$=V$+"W"
1130GOSUB1460:PRINT"LINK CALCULATION":G
OSUB 1460
1140PRINT"SITE CO-ORDINATES ";SL$","LR$
1150PRINT"SATELLITE POSITION ";LS$
1160PRINT"MAGNETIC VARIATION ";V$
1170GOSUB 1460
1180R=EL:GOSUB 1540:N=DG:GOSUB 1680:EL=
M
1190PRINT"ELEVATION = ";EL" DEGREES"
1200R=AZ:GOSUB 1540:N=DG:GOSUB 1680:AZ=
M
1210PRINT"TRUE AZIMUTH = ";AZ" DEGREES"
1220R=CB:GOSUB 1540:N=DG:GOSUB 1680:CB=
M
1230PRINT"COMPASS BEARING = ";CB" DEGRE
ES"
1240N=PD:GOSUB 1680:PD=M
1250PRINT"PATH DISTANCE = ";PD" KM"
1260RETURN
1270
1280REM OUTPUTB SUBROUTINE
1290N=FS:GOSUB1680:FS=M
1300PRINT"FREE SPACE LOSS = ";FS" DB"
1310N=GA:GOSUB1680:GA=M
1320PRINT"ANTENNA GAIN = ";GA" DBI"
1330N=TT:GOSUB1680:TT=M
1340PRINT"TOTAL NOISE TEMPERATURE = ";T
T" K"
1350N=GT:GOSUB1680:GT=M
1360PRINT"FIGURE OF MERIT = ";GT" DB"
1370N=CN:GOSUB1680:CN=M
1380PRINT"C/N RATIO = ";CN" DB"
1390N=SU:GOSUB1680:SU=M
1400PRINT"S/N RATIO (UNWEIGHTED) = ";SU
" DB"
1410N=SW:GOSUB1680:SW=M
1420PRINT"S/N RATIO (WEIGHTED) = ";SW"
DB"
1430RETURN
1440
1450REM DRAW LINE SUBROUTINE
1460PRINT"*****************************
*********"
1470RETURN
1480
1490REM DEGREES TO RADIANS SUBROUTINE
1500R=DG*P/180
```

```
1510RETURN
1520
1530REM RADIANS TO DEGREES SUBROUTINE
1540DG=180/P*R
1550RETURN
1560
1570REM ARC-COS SUBROUTINE
1580AC=-ATN(X/SQR(-X*X+1))+P/2
1590RETURN
1600
1610REM INPUT SUBROUTINE
1620INPUT A$:A=VAL(A$)
1630IF A=0 AND A$>"0" THEN A$=""
1640IF A<LO OR A>HI OR A$="" THEN 1620
1650RETURN
1660
1670REM ROUNDING SUBROUTINE
1680PL=2:M=INT(N*10^PL+0.5)/10^PL
1690RETURN
1700
1710REM OPTION SUBROUTINE
1720INPUT K$
1730IF K$<>"Y" AND K$<>"N" THEN 1720
1740RETURN
```

Program design philosophy

Program 5.1 was designed with the intention that it would work satis-factorily on any machine into which it was typed. This was achieved by catering for the machine with the lowest common denominator and restricting the BASIC language, of which there are many 'dialects', to a universal subset of keywords. If the program runs on such a machine then it will almost certainly work on more sophisticated machines. There-fore, the program will operate successfully on early Commodore PET and Apple II machines right through to today's modern computers. The restrictions present on many early machines, and some modern, are as follows:

1 No arc cos function (ACS). This can be derived from ATN by a subroutine.
2 Restriction of program line length to two 'on screen' lines of forty characters.
3 Restriction of variable names to two characters in length.
4 Do not support 'Procedures' only subroutines with no parameter passing.
5 Restriction to upper case characters only.
6 Non-standardization of printer on/off commands (unfortunately this cannot be overcome without simple programming knowledge).
7 Memory restrictions. (Computers with as low as 8 K of available memory should be sufficient.)

For those with machines supporting the superior BBC version of BASIC a separate program, Program 5.2, is provided complete with full printer options, which is considerably shorter in length.

Typing in the program

Type in the program *exactly* as it appears on the listing. The listing has been photo-reduced from the original well tested program and contains no known errors. If the program does not work, then there is a high probability of a typing error. Even a small insignificant typing error is sufficient to render the program unworkable. When you get the program running correctly, use the command, SAVE 'LINK' to save the program to tape or disc for later use. Type LOAD 'LINK' to load it back into the computer and type RUN to start the program.

Using the program

The program is very easy to use and simply prompts the user to enter the relevant data in the specified units in order to calculate the link budget. Remember to enter longitudes west of Greenwich as negative values (e.g. 3°W would be entered − 3), 3°E would be entered + 3 or just 3). Latitudes in the southern hemisphere are entered as negative values. The order, with typical values, is as follows:

Program 5.2   Linked budget calculation (BBC BASIC version)

```
>LIST
   10REM*******************************
   20REM*                             *
   30REM*  LINKED BUDGET CALCULATOR   *
   40REM*        (BBC BASIC)          *
   50REM*       DJ Stephenson         *
   60REM*                             *
   70REM*******************************
   80MODE 7
   90@%=&0102020A:REM 2 Decimal places
  100PROCinit
  110PROCline
  120PROCinputA
  130IF opt%<3 THEN PROCinputB
  140PROCcalcA
  150IF Elev<0 THEN PRINT"Satellite belo
w horizon":GOTO 250
  160IF opt%<3 THEN PROCcalcB
  170pr%=FNopt("YyNn","Output to printer
 (Y/N)?")
  180CLS
  190IF pr%<3 THEN VDU2
  200PROCoutputA
  210IF opt%<3 THEN PROCoutputB
  220PROCline
  230VDU3
  240@%=&0000090A:REM default setting
  250opt%=FNopt("YyNn","Repeat program (
Y/N)?")
  260IF opt%<3 THEN 80
  270END
  280
  290DEF PROCinit
  300PROCline:PRINT"LINKED BUDGET CALCUL
ATOR":PRINT TAB(20)" by DJ Stephenson":P
ROCline
  310opt%=FNopt("YyNn","Require FULL lin
k calculation (Y/N)?"):PRINT
  320PRINT"INPUT FORMAT : All values +ve
 except"
  330PRINT"a) Longitudes WEST -ve"
  340PRINT"b) Southern hemisphere latitu
des -ve"
  350PRINT"c) Magnetic variation WEST -v
e"
  360ENDPROC
  370
  380DEF PROCinputA
  390PRINT"Enter longitude of satellite
(deg)":LS=FNip(-180,180)
  400PRINT"Enter longitude of site (deg)
":LR=FNip(-180,180)
  410PRINT"Enter latitude of site (deg)"
:SL=FNip(-90,90)
  420PRINT"Enter local magnetic variatio
n (deg)":var=FNip(-60,60)
  430ENDPROC
  440
  450DEF PROCinputB
  460PRINT"Enter channel frequency (GHz)
":chfreq=FNip(10,14)
  470PRINT"Enter antenna diameter (metre
s)":dia=FNip(0.2,5)
  480PRINT"Enter antenna efficientcy (%)
":P=FNip(10,100)
  490PRINT"Enter antenna noise temperatu
```

```
re (K)":Tant=FNip(1,200)
  500PRINT"Enter LNB noise figure (dB)":
NF=FNip(0.5,3)
  510PRINT"Enter EIRP figure (dbW) ":EIR
P=FNip(1,200)
  520PRINT"Enter bandwidth of signal (MH
z)":BW=FNip(5,100)
  530PRINT"Enter highest video frequency
 (MHz)":VF=FNip(3,30)
  540PRINT"Enter deviation (MHz)":dev=FN
ip(5,100)
  550PRINT"Enter pre-emphasis improvemen
t (dB)":PE=FNip(1,5)
  560PRINT"Enter weighting factor (dB)":
WF=FNip(1,50)
  570ENDPROC
  580
  590DEFPROCcalcA
  600A=LS-LR:sign=SGN(A):A=ABS(A)
  610A=RAD(A):B=RAD(SL):var=RAD(var)
  620C=ACS(COS(A)*COS(B))
  630Elev=ATN((COS(C)-0.151269)/SIN(C))
  640IF Elev<0 THEN 720
  650Azimuth=ATN(TAN(A)/SIN(B))
  660Azimuth=PI-sign*Azimuth
  670Compass=Azimuth-var
  680IF SL<0 THEN Azimuth=Azimuth-PI:Com
pass=Compass-PI
  690IF Azimuth<0 THEN Azimuth=Azimuth+2
*PI
  700IF Compass<0 THEN Compass=Compass+2
*PI
  710Pathdist=(42164*SIN(C))/COS(Elev)
  720ENDPROC
  730
  740DEFPROCcalcB
  750W=3*10^8/(chfreq*10^9)
  760A=20*LOG(4*PI*Pathdist*1000/W)
  770Ga=10*LOG((((PI*dia)^2)*P)/((W^2)*1
00))
  780Flnb=10^(NF/10)
  790Tlnb=(Flnb-1)*290
  800Ttot=Tant+Tlnb
  810GT=10*LOG((10^(Ga/10))/Ttot)
  820NB=10*LOG(BW*10^6)
  830CN=EIRP+GT+228.6-NB-A
  840FMI=10*LOG(1.5*((dev/VF)^2)*(BW/VF)
)
  850SNuw=CN+FMI+PE
  860SNw=SNuw+WF
  870ENDPROC
  880
  890DEFPROCoutputA
  900SL$=STR$(ABS(SL)):LS$=STR$(ABS(LS))
:LR$=STR$(ABS(LR)):var$=STR$(ABS(DEG(var
)))
  910IF SL<0 THEN SL$=SL$+"S" ELSE SL$=S
L$+"N"
  920IF LS<0 THEN LS$=LS$+"W" ELSE LS$=L
S$+"E"
  930IF LR<0 THEN LR$=LR$+"W" ELSE LR$=L
R$+"E"
  940IF var<0 THEN var$=var$+"W" ELSE va
r$=var$+"E"
  950PROCline:PRINT"LINK CALCULATION":PR
OCline
  960PRINT"Site co-ordinates ";SL$","LR$
  970PRINT"Satellite position ";LS$
  980PRINT"Magnetic variation ";var$
```

```
 990PROCline
1000PRINT"Elevation = ";DEG(Elev)" degr
ees"
1010PRINT"True azimuth = ";DEG(Azimuth)
" degrees"
1020PRINT"Compass bearing = ";DEG(Compa
ss)" degrees"
1030PRINT"Path distance = ";Pathdist" K
m"
1040ENDPROC
1050
1060DEF PROCoutputB
1070PRINT"Free space loss = ";A" dB"
1080PRINT"Antenna gain = ";Ga" dBi"
1090PRINT"Total noise temperature = ";T
tot" K"
1100PRINT"Figure of merit = ";GT" dB"
1110PRINT"C/N ratio = ";CN" dB"
1120PRINT"S/N ratio (unweighted) = ";SN
uw" dB"
1130PRINT"S/N ratio (weighted) = ";SNw"
dB"
1140ENDPROC
1150
1160DEFPROCline
1170PRINT STRING$(39,"_"):ENDPROC
1180
1190DEF FNip(min,max)
1200REPEAT
1210INPUT A$:A=VAL(A$)
1220IF A=0 AND A$>"0" THEN A$=""
1230UNTIL A>=min AND A<=max AND A$<>""
1240=A
1250
1260DEF FNopt(K$,M$)
1270PRINT M$" ";:K%=0:REPEAT:F$=GET$
1280IF F$<>"" K%=INSTR(K$,F$)
1290UNTIL K%>0
1300PRINT F$
1310=K%
```

1 Longitude of satellite (degrees).
2 Longitude of receiving site (degrees).
3 Latitude of receiving site (degrees).
4 Local magnetic variation (degrees);   (typically 4°W to 10°W in UK).
5 Channel frequency (GHz).
6 Antenna diameter (metres).
7 Antenna efficiency (per cent);   (typically 55 per cent to 80 per cent).
8 Antenna noise temperature (° K);   (approx 30 to 100° K).
9 LNB noise figure (dB).
10 EIRP level (dBW).
11 Bandwidth of signal (MHz);   (typically 27 MHz).
12 Highest video frequency (MHz);   (5 MHz for PAL).
13 Deviation (MHz);   (typically 15 MHz to 28 MHz).
14 Pre-emphasis improvement (dB);   (typically 2 dB).
15 Weighting factor (dB);   (PAL I signals 11 dB, MAC 13 dB).

The end result of a program run will be the final screen display containing the following information:

1 Receiving site coordinates.
2 Satellite position.
3 Magnetic variation.

Link calculation details:

4 Elevation (degrees).
5 True azimuth (degrees).
6 Azimuth compass bearing (corrected), (°).
7 Path distance to satellite (km).
8 Free space loss (dB).
9 Antenna gain (dBi).
10 Total noise temperature (° K).
11 Figure of merit (dB).
12 Carrier to noise ratio (dB).
13 Unweighted signal to noise ratio (dB).
14 Weighted signal to noise ratio (dB).

Conclusion

This chapter has, unfortunately, had to cover some fairly complicated concepts that to some may appear irrelevant to the practice of satellite TVRO installation. However, those that have persevered will have acquired a sound basic knowledge of the underlying principles and the realization of how various parameters interact. This should help the installation technician to deal with most potential technical problems that may arise in the field and to be reasonably competent in the specification of equipment to fit any need.

6 Installation: surveying the receiving site

Introduction

The purpose of the rather pretentiously named 'site survey' is to check out the lie of the land and offer the customer the maximum amount of choice as to the location of the dish, bearing in mind that microwave signals will not pass through buildings, trees, etc. Some customers like their dishes to be unobtrusive whilst others like to advertise the fact that they have one. If properly conducted, a site survey can eliminate wasted journeys for tools and equipment not loaded onto the service vehicle. The need for a formal survey differs from region to region and listed below are the main types of terrain likely to be encountered, together with advice on the course of action.

1 *Flat open countryside* – This is the ideal terrain and presents no problems even to DIY installation. Providing you know the rough direction of the required medium power or DBS satellite, it may be possible to dispense with the formal site survey altogether since no obstructions of the geo-arc are likely to be encountered.

2 *City areas and large towns* – Locations in towns or cities with high rise flats, large industrial complexes, or high density housing may present problems when choosing an antenna mounting location. For example, many towns in northern England have rows of terraced houses built on hillsides. Because of the elevated nature of the adjacent row of houses it may not be possible to achieve the necessary clearance of the next rooftop using a standard wall mounting bracket. A similar difficulty can occur when attempting to find a gap between adjacent 'tower blocks' in city areas. Here, an accurate site survey is essential since inaccuracies of even a degree or two in siting the antenna may result in failure, leaving an unsightly array of mounting holes as evidence. It is not rare for so-called 'professionals' to do this, and in some cases they have even informed customers that reception is not possible when an accurate azimuth/elevation calculation and precision survey has often proved them wrong. The installation can then proceed with confidence reducing the risk of the aforementioned 'Laurel and Hardy' performance which does little to instil customer confidence in your company. Where tall buildings or trees

are blocking, or partially blocking, the line of sight to the required satellite the customer should be informed that reception is not possible or likely to be degraded.

3   *Leafy suburbs and villages* – The main problem here is trees, requiring a varying degree of accuracy in site survey work. It is important to remember that trees grow in girth as well as height and the customer should be informed if future reception is likely to be degraded as a result of tree growth. If the offending trees are on the customer's land they may agree to lop off certain branches from time to time.

4   *Highland regions* – In mountainous terrain such as that encountered in the north of Scotland, siting an antenna can be critical. Other than obvious blocking problems by mountains, the following additional complications arise:

(a)   EIRP levels often fall off in these northern areas and the need for a larger antenna leads to correspondingly more accurate alignment requirements (remember beamwidth in Chapter 2).

(b)   Elevation angles to the geo-arc are low in northern regions increasing the risk of blocking of the signal by mountains.

Again, a formal link calculation and site survey are recommended in the majority of cases.

Finding satellite coordinates

Each geo-stationary satellite is located above the equator at a height of some 36 000 km and its position is given as a simple longitudinal position either west or east of the Greenwich meridian (0°). From this information we need to look up from records, or calculate using simple trigonometry, the required azimuth and elevation angles to capture a required satellite's signals from any particular location within the service area. The receiving site is described by a unique set of coordinates called latitude and longitude. For accurate information on these coordinates refer to an ordnance survey map of your local area.

Whether multi-satellite or fixed satellite reception is the object of the survey the *AZ/EL* angles for each required satellite must be checked for obstructions such as buildings or trees. There are four items of information, 1 to 4 shown below, needed to perform an accurate receiving site survey. Two of these need to be calculated, or looked up from records, for each required satellite before arriving at the customer's address. The keeping of detailed records of pointing angles for each satellite will alleviate the need for repeat calculations since angles will not vary significantly across a small local service area. A programmable scientific calculator with continuous memory or a computer will help here. If you find difficulty with the calculations there are many mathematically inclined individuals who will be delighted to help you.

1   *The geostationary position of the satellite* – For example, the Astra cluster of satellites are positioned above the equator over Zaire, 19.2° east of south of the Greenwich meridian. The BSB satellite is off the coast of Brazil at 31.0° west of south. Appendix 3 gives this information for a range of the more popular satellites.
2   *Elevation* – The angle of inclination from the horizontal to the satellite line of sight and given by Equation 5.1 in Chapter 5.
3   *Azimuth* – The bearing of the satellite depending on the location of the receiving site and given by Equation 5.2.
4   *The local magnetic variation* – True south can be offset by a few degrees from magnetic south depending on the location of the receiving site, and varies by a small amount each year.

Magnetic variation

The indicated north on a compass can vary considerably from true north depending on the geographical location. The effect is known as *magnetic variation* in nautical terms or *magnetic declination* in scientific terms. Variation is said to be easterly if the direction of magnetic north lies to the east of the true meridian, and westerly if it lies to the west. Points of equal variation on the globe are contoured with *isogonal lines*. Where true north and magnetic north are the same (i.e. variation = 0), the contour is called the *Agonic line*. Magnetic variation is subject to three types of change:

1   *Secular change* – a continuous alteration decreasing by about nine minutes of arc annually in the UK.
2   *Annual change* – small seasonal fluctuations.
3   *Diurnal change* – a daily fluctuation which increases with latitude.

Items 2 and 3 can be neglected for our purposes since they are relatively insignificant and contribute a worst case error of about a quarter of a degree. Angles are small as this cannot be accurately resolved on most hand held compasses. Thus item 1, the secular change, is the most important.

If the variation is westerly, the variation is negative, therefore the correction to be applied to the compass is positive. The value is added to the indicated compass bearing to obtain the true bearing. Likewise if the variation is easterly, the variation is positive therefore the correction to be applied to the compass is negative. The value is subtracted from the indicated compass bearing to find the true bearing. Figure 6.1 clearly illustrates this point. Most good sighting compasses have a rotating dial which can be set to compensate for local variation and thus indicate true bearings. In the UK true north/south can vary between 4° and 10° clockwise from magnetic north/south, depending on location and this further increases by about nine minutes clockwise each year. Current information can be obtained from the latest edition Ordnance Survey maps (or similar) for your area.

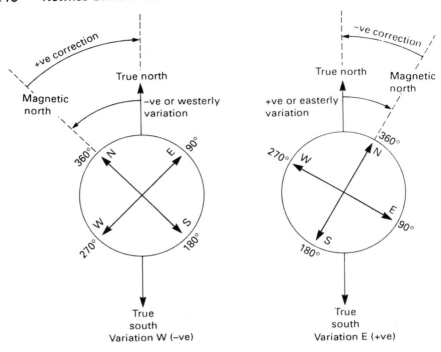

Figure 6.1   *Magnetic variation and compass readings*

Ordnance Survey maps

Local area Ordnance Survey maps, or their overseas counterparts, are singly the most useful source of information regarding accurate site latitude and longitude coordinates and can be consulted at your local library. Latitudes are given at the sides of the map and longitudes are

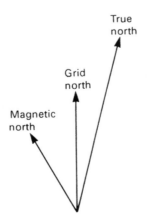

Figure 6.2   *Relationship between grid north and true north*

given at the top or bottom of the maps. The current magnetic variation for your local area is obtained from the top centre of the map, although this variation is in relation to grid north and not true north. An additional correction factor is given on the maps, typically about one degree, and this should be added to the variation between grid north and magnetic north to find the total magnetic variation. Figure 6.2 illustrates this point.

If an Ordnance Survey map is not conveniently to hand the appropriate magnetic variation can be estimated to a reasonable degree of accuracy in the UK from Figure 6.3.

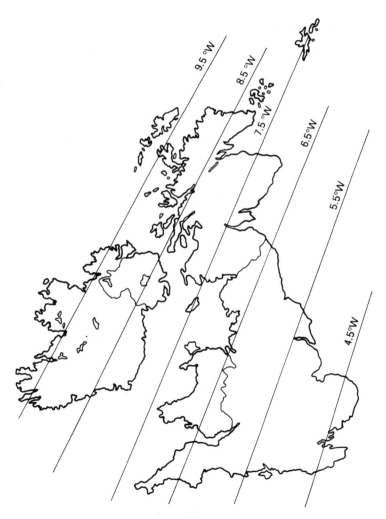

Figure 6.3   *Isogonal map of UK and Eire*

Site survey computer program

The site survey calculations, when occasionally needed, can be performed by computer in a fraction of a second for any geographical location and any satellite location. A conveniently short program, Program 6.1, written using a universal dialect of BASIC and using the same design philosophy as that indicated in Chapter 5, will perform all the necessary angle calculations for both present and future satellites. For those with machines supporting BBC BASIC an even shorter version is provided. However, if you have the full linked budget program (Programs 5.1 or Program 5.2) available, these short-form programs will not be needed since an option is already provided for angle calculations only.

Using the satellite finder program

It is important when using the program to remember that longitudes west of Greenwich (0°) are entered as negative values. For example Wirral, Merseyside is 3° west so it entered as −3. Longitudes east of Greenwich are entered as positive values. Grossly ridiculous inputs will not be accepted. Follow the same instructions for typing and saving the program as that given for Program 5.1 and 5.2 but remember to use a different program filename! Programs 6.1 and 6.2 are simply abbreviated versions of those given in Chapter 5. An example of the type of data required for input is shown below:

1 On running the program, the first prompt asks for the longitude of the satellite. Astra 1A and 1B are 19.2° east of south. This is a positive value according to the rules above, so enter 19.2.
2 The second prompt asks for the longitude of the site. For Merseyside, UK, this is 3° west so is entered at −3.
3 The third prompt is for the latitude of the site. For Merseyside, UK, this is 53.33° north, so enter 53.33.
4 Finally, the prompt for local magnetic variation is displayed. From ordnance survey maps this is 6.5° west for Merseyside, so enter −6.5.

The program will calculate the elevation, true azimuth, compass bearing and path distance. With the example data given you should get 25.74°, 153.03°, 158.53° and 39 001.1 km respectively. Simply type 'RUN' to repeat the program. A printout can be obtained on the BBC BASIC version by pressing 'CTRL' and 'B' keys simultaneously prior to typing 'RUN'. CTRL C disables the printer again. With the universal BASIC version you will need to look up the printer on/off commands in the instruction book; these commands unfortunately are not standardized.

Azimuth survey

Once the magnetically corrected angle is known, the only piece of equipment required to perform an accurate azimuth survey is a compass. The

Program 6.1   Satellite Finder Program (Universal BASIC version)

```
>LIST
  10REM*********************************
  20REM*                                *
  30REM*        SATELLITE FINDER         *
  40REM*    (UNIVERSAL BASIC SUBSET)     *
  50REM*        DJ STEPHENSON            *
  60REM*                                *
  70REM*********************************
  80P=3.14159265
  90GOSUB 490:PRINT"SATELLITE FINDER BY
DJ STEPHENSON":GOSUB 490
 100PRINT"INPUT FORMAT : ALL VALUES +VE
EXCEPT"
 110PRINT"LONGITUDES WEST -VE"
 120PRINT"SOUTHERN HEMISPHERE LATITUDES
-VE"
 130PRINT"MAGNETIC VARIATION WEST -VE"
 140GOSUB 500:PRINT"ENTER LONGITUDE OF
SATELLITE (DEG)"
 150LO=-180:HI=180:GOSUB 620:LS=A
 160PRINT"ENTER LONGITUDE OF SITE (DEG)
"
 170GOSUB 620:LR=A
 180PRINT"ENTER LATITUDE OF SITE (DEG)"
 190LO=-90:HI=90:GOSUB 620:SL=A
 200PRINT"ENTER LOCAL MAGNETIC VARIATIO
N (DEG)"
 210GOSUB 620:V=A
 220A=LS-LR:SN=SGN(A):A=ABS(A)
 230DG=A:GOSUB 530:A=R
 240DG=SL:GOSUB 530:B=R
 250X=COS(A)*COS(B):GOSUB 590:C=AC
 260EL=ATN((COS(C)-0.151269)/SIN(C))
 270IF EL<0 THEN PRINT"Satellite over h
orizon":GOTO 460
 280AZ=ATN(TAN(A)/SIN(B))
 290AZ=P-SN*AZ
 300IF SL<0 THEN AZ=AZ-P
 310IF AZ<0 THEN AZ=AZ+2*P
 320PD=(42164*SIN(C))/COS(EL)
 330DC=ABS(ATN((3964*SIN(B))/(22300+396
4*(1-COS(B)))))
 340GOSUB 490
 350R=EL:GOSUB 560:N=DG:GOSUB 670:EL=M
 360R=AZ:GOSUB 560:N=DG:GOSUB 670:AZ=M
 370CB=AZ-V
 380R=DC:GOSUB 560:N=DG:GOSUB 670:DC=M
 390N=PD:GOSUB 670:PD=M
 400PRINT"ELEVATION = ";EL" DEGREES"
 410PRINT"TRUE AZIMUTH = ";AZ" DEGREES"
 420PRINT"COMPASS BEARING = ";CB" DEGRE
ES"
 430PRINT"DECLINATION = ";DC" DEGREES"
 440PRINT"PATH DISTANCE = ";PD" KM"
 450GOSUB 500
 460PRINT"TYPE 'RUN' TO REPEAT PROGRAM"
;
 470END
 480REM ****************************
 490REM DRAW LINE SUBROUTINE
 500FOR N=1 TO 39:PRINT"-";:NEXT:PRINT
 510RETURN
 520REM DEGREES TO RADIANS SUBROUTINE
 530R=DG*P/180
 540RETURN
 550REM RADIANS TO DEGREES SUBROUTINE
 560DG=180/P*R
```

```
570RETURN
580REM ARC-COS SUBROUTINE
590AC=-ATN(X/SQR(-X*X+1))+P/2
600RETURN
610REM INPUT SUBROUTINE
620INPUT A$:A=VAL(A$)
630IF A=0 AND A$>"0" THEN A$=""
640IF A<LO OR A>HI OR A$="" THEN 620
650RETURN
660REM ROUNDING SUBROUTINE
670PL=2:M=INT(N*10^PL+0.5)/10^PL
680RETURN
```

Program 6.2   Satellite Finder Program (BBC BASIC version)

```
>LIST
   10REM*********************************
   20REM*                               *
   30REM*      SATELLITE FINDER         *
   40REM*        (BBC BASIC)            *
   50REM*        DJ Stephenson          *
   60REM*                               *
   70REM*********************************
   80MODE 7
   90@%=&0102020A:REM 2 Decimal places
  100PROCline:PRINT"SATELLITE FINDER by
DJ Stephenson":PROCline
  110PRINT"INPUT FORMAT : All values +ve
 except"
  120PRINT"a) Longitudes WEST -ve"
  130PRINT"b) Southern hemisphere latitu
des -ve"
  140PRINT"c) Magnetic variation WEST -v
e"
  150PRINT:PRINT"Enter Longitude of Sate
llite (deg)":LS=FNip(-180,180)
  160PRINT"Enter Longitude of Site (deg)
":LR=FNip(-180,180)
  170PRINT"Enter Latitude of Site (deg)"
:SL=FNip(-90,90)
  180PRINT"Enter Local Magnetic Variatio
n (deg)":var=FNip(-90,90)
  190A=LS-LR:sign=SGN(A):A=ABS(A)
  200A=RAD(A):B=RAD(SL)
  210C=ACS(COS(A)*COS(B))
  220Elev=ATN((COS(C)-0.151269)/SIN(C))
  230IF Elev<0 THEN PRINT"Satellite belo
w horizon":GOTO 360
  240Azimuth=ATN(TAN(A)/SIN(B))
  250Azimuth=PI-sign*Azimuth
  260IF SL<0 THEN Azimuth=Azimuth-PI
  270IF Azimuth<0 THEN Azimuth=Azimuth+2
*PI
  280Pathdist=(42164*SIN(C))/COS(Elev)
  290Declination=ABS(ATN((3964*SIN(B))/(
22300+3964*(1-COS(B)))))
  300PROCline
  310PRINT"Elevation = ";DEG(Elev)" degr
ees"
  320PRINT"True azimuth = ";DEG(Azimuth)
" degrees"
  330PRINT"Compass bearing = ";DEG(Azimu
th)-var" degrees"
  340PRINT"Declination = ";DEG(Declinati
on)" degrees"
  350PRINT"Path distance = ";Pathdist" K
m"
  360PRINT:PRINT"Type 'RUN' to repeat pr
ogram ";
  370@%=&0000090A:REM default setting
  380END
  390
  400DEFPROCline
  410PRINT STRING$(39,"_"):ENDPROC
  420
  430DEF FNip(min,max)
  440REPEAT
  450INPUT A$:A=VAL(A$)
  460IF A=0 AND A$>"0" THEN A$=""
  470UNTIL A>=min AND A<=max AND A$<>""
  480=A
```

cheap Christmas cracker variety, although adequate in some open aspect areas, is a poor substitute for a quality sighting compass. These are usually equipped with a movable graduated dial, mirror and sighting line or notch to enable some distant object to be used as a reference to the required bearing. The magnetically corrected bearing is set on the compass so that the sighting line corresponds with the satellites azimuthal position. Correctly orientating the compass so that the needle lines up with the N/S markings will then give the required bearing at the sighting line as shown in the simplified diagram, Figure 6.4. When conducting an azimuth survey with a compass stay well clear of metal objects which affect compass readings. Stray influences can be discovered by moving about in the general area to see if the compass needle varies considerably.

Elevation survey

The items of equipment needed to perform an elevation survey are a device called an inclinometer and a sighting bar (normally a large spirit level). Inclinometers vary in design from a glorified protractor and plumb line to sophisticated moiré pattern types which can be accurate to a fraction of a degree. The choice is yours but the latter type is well worth the extra money in view of its further use in the setting of antenna elevation angles.

The inclinometer is set, according to the manufacturer's instructions, to the required elevation angle and placed on a sighting bar. The bar is inclined until either the moiré patterns are parallel or, with the cheaper type, the required elevation is indicated on the dial. By looking along the bar, as shown in Figure 6.5, any obstructions can be noted. Another method used by some installers for ground erected polar mounts is to attach a piece of pipe or a spent biro casing to an old camera tripod. The elevation angle is set for each required satellite using the inclinometer and if clear sky is seen when viewing through the tube then reception will be satisfactory. For DIY surveying, a makeshift inclinometer can be made from a piece of wood and a plastic protractor mounted at right angles to it, as shown in Figure 6.6. The reading coinciding with the weighted string is the elevation angle of the piece of wood relative to ground.

Single satellite reception

A fixed wall mounted antenna is the one most commonly encountered and is often part of a manufacturer's package for single satellite reception. A site survey typically involves running up and down ladders at various points of the dwelling checking the line of sight. Since wall mounted dishes can be rotated through 180° a south facing wall is not essential. Complications can commonly arise with some dwellings and the solution is to dispense with the wall mounting bracket and specify pole mounting. Common scenarios are listed below with the appropriate solution.

Problem:

The awkward customer who does not want the antenna mounted on the front or sides of the house even though this is the most convenient position.

Solution:

Check if the antenna can be mounted on an outbuilding or pole in the rear garden. Finally if this is not feasible check the minimum height pole required to capture signals from over the roof apex. This of course will depend on the roof pitch which can be easily measured with an inclinometer.

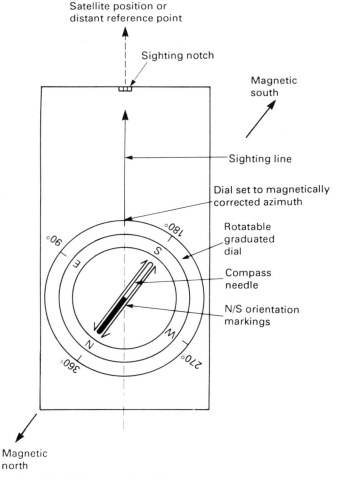

Figure 6.4 *Simplified diagram of a sighting compass*

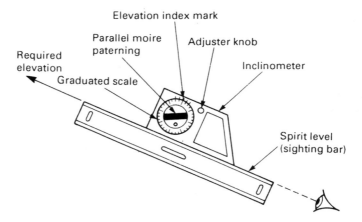

Figure 6.5　*Using an inclinometer for elevation surveying*

Problem:
>The most suitable mounting position, with a wall bracket, is the front of the house but the dwelling is of the dormer bungalow type with tiled upper front walls or wooden planks. A secure mounting is not possible on such a surface.

Solution:
>The antenna may be positioned, using a pole and T & K bracket to the side of the house (usually brick). The length of the pole must be such that the roof pitch, where necessary, is taken into account. In some cases a wide chimney construction emerges from a flat roof section below roof apex height. This is sometimes adequate for fixing a standard wall bracket.

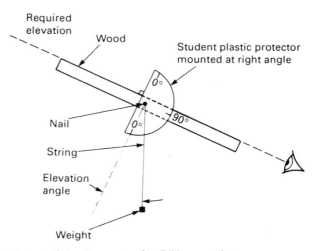

Figure 6.6　*Makeshift inclinometer for DIY surveying*

Problem:

The wall mounting bracket cannot be placed on a suitable wall because part of the dish aperture is likely to be obstructed by the eaves. This is a common problem encountered with terraced housing where the line of the housing row is the same or close to the required azimuth bearing.

Solution:

The antenna will need to be mounted using a T & K bracket and pole to lift the antenna out and above the eaves. If possible always site at the rear of the house in preference to the front. It is not normally advisable to pole mount dishes on chimneys with aerial lashing kits as done with terrestrial TV aerials. The wind loading effect, on even a relatively small dish, can be such that the whole structure may become unstable and dangerous. Especially so if further compounded by poor mortar condition on older chimneys. Planning permission is also required for mounting above roof apex height.

Problem:

Adequate line of sight clearance above an adjacent structure prevents the standard wall mounting bracket from being used.

Solution:

Use a T & K wall bracket and pole to achieve the extra height or mount the pole in the attic. A special weatherproof tile is available for the pole exit from the roof space.

When specifing these alternative forms of mounting it is important to inform the customer that an extra charge, over and above the standard installation charge, is required to cover the extra work and materials used. It is also important to remember that some manufacturer's packaged systems are unsuitable for pole mounting and the customer should be advised accordingly.

Multi-satellite reception

Large antenna multi-satellite systems designed to include reception from the present crop of low power satellites are normally ground or patio mounted but later generations of polar mount dishes designed to receive only medium to high power satellites are expected to be much smaller with the possibility of wall or elevated pole mounting. For multi-satellite reception the surveying process would need to be repeated for each required satellite. It is surprising how few domestic locations are suited for multi-satellite reception, due to obstruction of part of the geo-arc. However in many cases 'windows' can be found to receive signals from a reduced number of the more popular satellites. It is important to discuss this with customers at the time of the site survey so they are in no doubt as to the blocked satellites. For this type of survey there are various cardboard cutout creations that can be used to simultaneously check the

Required satellite name	Azimuth angle (magnetically corrected) (degrees)	Elevation angle (degrees)	Tick box as appropriate			
			Azimuth OK?	Elevation OK?	Receive	
					Yes	No

Figure 6.7   *Checklist for multi-satellite reception*

line of sight to each satellite. Unfortunately these are rarely up to date and are short lived. It is advisable to use strong reliable instruments in conjunction with a checklist of the type outlined in Figure 6.7. As the coordinates of each required satellite are checked the form can be filled in. The results will clearly indicate which of the required satellites in the geo-arc will be received satisfactorily. The forms can be either printed or photocopied from a partially completed master. Multi-satellite coordinate surveying is not as tedious as it seems since it will be obvious when part of the geo-arc is unobstructed thereby increasing the rate of box ticking without using instruments.

Site plans and survey maps

The need for a site plan varies, but in most cases it is not considered necessary. One case where it may be necessary to spend some considerable time drawing a detailed plan is where the installation is to be carried out by persons other than the surveyor. However, once the antenna position has been decided the area can be simply marked with chalk or a stick. A list of required tools and materials not always carried on the service vehicle is normally sufficient in practice.

Distribution amplifiers

On the site survey always ask if a multi-point distribution amplifier is installed for terrestrial TV. The likelihood is that the customer will want the RF output of the satellite receiver to be distributed along with his normal TV channels for viewing in a number of rooms. The extra materials and installation time will need to be charged for in the initial quote.

Planning permission

In the UK, it may not be necessary to apply for planning permission for a single antenna mounted below roof apex height unless it exceeds 90 cm in diameter. However, if the receiving site is in a conservation area or the dwelling is a listed building of architectural interest the customer should be advised to check with the local council planning department. Many councils have their own guidelines with regard to satellite installations and these are reputed to be up to seven A4-sized pages in length! Antennae over 90 cm normally require planning permission if within public view or in sight of neighbours.

Vandalism

When surveying it is also necessary to judge the likelihood of vandalism. Obviously, if a ground mounted antenna is located in the front garden of a dwelling close to a licensed premises, the likelihood of vandalism is high. Always try to mount antenna out of open sight or at such a height that one person standing on another's shoulders cannot reach the antenna. That is to say mount over 'two drunks high' (12 ft). It is really surprising the lengths vandals will go to perfect their 'art' and satellite dishes potentially attract a lot of attention.

7 Installation: antenna mounting and cabling

Introduction

This chapter is basically a practical 'nuts and bolts' guide to the assembly and physical mounting of a variety of satellite brackets and poles and discusses the principal tools, equipment, cabling and fixing methods needed to execute a professional installation that will last for years. It is not really necessary to understand the finer details of satellite TV to effect a perfectly adequate installation. The approach adopted is designed to cater for the vast majority of installations and will assume:

1   No previous knowledge.
2   No tools or equipment have been acquired.
3   That work is restricted to the popular types of equipment sold by domestic electronics retailers. (Not SMATV equipment.)
4   Antennae are mounted below roof apex height (usually no planning permission required).

Insurance

Before starting any satellite installation work for the general public ensure that you are adequately insured. Public liability insurance cover should be taken out, along with employee liability if someone is working for you. The latter is a legal requirement. At the time of writing, cover to the value of one million pounds is the recommended level. Further insurance against personal injury is also wise, due to the potentially dangerous nature of the ladder work.

Installation staff

Ideally, an installation team should consist of a technician and a labourer skilled in ladder agility. Unfortunately, many companies with an eye on profits rather than safety insist on single person installation. Although, it is perfectly possible for the job to be performed adequately by one person it is not to be encouraged. In any case, a skilled and coordinated two-person team can complete the job in approximately half the time.

Customer relations

Most customers are interested in the background technical details of satellite TV, particularly in such matters as the satellite's height, geographical position, etc. This exchange of 'chit-chat' creates a friendly atmosphere in which to work and is often punctuated by regular cups of tea or coffee. Cowboy practices, such as the operation of 'ghetto blasters' or raucous singing irritates many customers and should be avoided. Installers should work as tidily as possible, using dust sheets for all interior drilling and should discuss with the customer the dish siting, cable route and method of cable entry.

Two points worth a mention; firstly, never conduct an installation if the householder or spouse is not present. It is not uncommon to install a system, after consultation with a teenage son or daughter, only to be asked to move the dish elsewhere on the householder's return. Secondly, avoid mounting an antenna above a doorway. Rain drips can saturate customers and their callers and may lead to a request for it to be moved at a later date.

Guarantees

It is customary to guarantee your work for a period of at least a year against wind altering the alignment of the dish or water penetrating the coax etc. It should be pointed out to the customer that this does not cover vandalism or freak weather conditions such as the force ten hurricanes experienced in the South of England in 1987. It is the customer's responsibility to insure against these risks.

Basic tools and equipment

It is never worthwhile skimping on tool prices, stick to established brand names associated with quality. Cheap imported 'noddy' tools are rarely adequate, except for the occasional domestic use.

Ladders

The most important requirements are a roof rack and a set of ladders. A versatile size is a 28 ft double or an equivalent triple section ladder, which extends a few feet above gutter height of the average house. Since heavy loads are not being carried class 3 domestic ladders are quite adequate and considerably cheaper than say those used by builders. Aluminium ones are light and easy to handle but ensure that the rungs are flat topped and inclined so that they are level when the ladder is at its recommended working angle. Round section rungs, such as the type often fitted to wooden ladders are liable to make your feet ache after only a short time. A 15 ft roof ladder is a necessity if working on sloping roofs, although in my experience such working is rarely needed. In any case at the time of writing, planning permission must be sought if a dish is to be mounted above roof apex height, so is best avoided. Many modern houses have flat garage roofs adjoining their walls so an additional single ladder or step ladder is required. I have found that a two way single/step ladder is the most versatile in these cases and can be used where the 28 ft double is either too high, when not extended, or the resulting slope is excessively large. Alternatively, a short single ladder and a dedicated step ladder can be acquired.

Safety precautions when using ladders

All ladders used should be equipped with non-slip feet and when erected should be perfectly vertical, looking from the front. The recommended ladder slope is 4:1 (vertical:horizontal). If it is necessary to use a steeper slope, due to say a restricted width alleyway then ensure that another person is holding the ladder or lash the top to prevent the ladder slipping sideways. In the other case where the slope is less than recommended ensure the feet are firmly wedged with blocks of stone or concrete. Often the base for the ladder is not level; to ensure that the ladder is not inclined sideways, pack or firmly wedge one of the feet as appropriate. When erecting wall mounted brackets, the top of the ladder can be securely lashed to the bracket using strong multi-wrapped luggage straps. This is particularly important in windy conditions. Never over-reach when working on ladders, be sure of your footing and balance at all times. If snow or frost is present then clear the area where the feet are to be positioned and as a further precaution a mixture of sand and salt should be scattered over the area. Never work on sloping roofs unless a roof ladder is used fitted with a bracket designed to securely overhang the ridge tiles.

Occasionally, where the dish is to be mounted on a high wall, such as the third storey of a maisonette, it is possible to hire large rope operated ladders which extend to 44 ft or more. These ladders are very heavy and two persons, at least, are needed to manipulate them into position! The first use of such ladders can be a fairly 'hair raising' experience due to the whip witnessed as they are ascended. The ladders seem to exhibit a life of their own in this respect, and the feeling is rather akin to that experienced whilst walking on a trampoline, albeit an elevated one! As experience is gained the initial terror wears off, but you should still treat them with the greatest respect. It's a long way down, and falls of over 40 ft are nearly always fatal. If you've not got a head for heights then subcontract the high altitude work.

Electric drills

An electric drill is used a lot in installation work for boring dish bracket and cable entry holes. When drilling wall mounting bracket holes it is vital that fixings be made into brick and not the mortar course, therefore a powerful hammer drill (650 W or greater) with at least a 13 mm ($\frac{1}{2}$ in) chuck is needed. There are a large variety of electric drills on the market to choose from, and below are some of the features provided:

1 Drilling / hammer drilling changeover facility.
2 Two-speed mechanical gearbox.
3 Continuously variable speed control.
4 Forward and reverse changeover switch.
5 Electronic torque control for electric screwdriving.
6 Soft start.
7 Safety handle.
8 Scaled drill depth stop.

For maximum versatility, a drill with all the above functions combined with a power rating of 650 W or greater is a good choice. The slow speed electric screwdriver facility can be useful for mounting small dishes with plastic plugs and screws. The drill is best connected to the mains via a quick release plug/socket and 30 m extension lead drum. Although most drills are double insulated, 'belt and braces' safety can be effected with the incorporation of a residual current circuit breaker plug or an isolation transformer.

Drill bits

Set out below in Table 7.1 is a list of commonly used drill bit sizes and length included in the average tool kit. The lengths specified are the minimum length, it does not matter if they are longer. Usually 380 mm length is sufficient to drill a standard cavity wall. If possible obtain the double spiral type (usually matt black finish), such as Rawlbor

Table 7.1 *Commonly used drill bit sizes*

Diameter (mm)	Min. length (mm)	Type	Principle use
8	120 mm	Masonry	Mounting holes
10	120 mm	Masonry	Mounting holes
14	120 mm	Masonry	Mounting holes
16	120 mm	Masonry	Mounting holes
8	150 mm	Auger	Cable entry
10	380 mm	Masonry	Cable entry
14	380 mm	Masonry	Multi-cable entry
18	380 mm	Masonry	Multi-cable entry

manufactured by the Rawlplug company. This design doubles the removal of spoil, resulting in faster, easier drilling and subsequently less wear on the drill and bit.

Extra tools and materials for installation work

Other useful tools and materials are:

1   An assortment of screwdrivers including cross point types.
2   Claw hammer.
3   Spirit level.
4   Craft knife or coax stripper.
5   Wire cutters.
6   A set of metric ring or combination, spanners (6 mm to 22 mm).
7   A pair of mole grips or pump pliers.
8   A metric socket set (optional).
9   A tool belt (saves a lot of footwork when working up ladders).
10 Solder gun (some receivers need special plugs soldering onto cable).
11 Rolls of self-amalgamating tape (weatherproofing outdoor connections).
12 Weatherproof rubber 'boots' (optional, to cover F connectors).
13 7 mm round section coax clips (CT100/H109F cables).
14 Assortment of larger clips for tacking up combination cables.
15 F connectors (twist-on type).
16 F to F connector line sockets.
17 Standard coax plugs.
18 Coax plug to coax plug line sockets.
19 Coax combiners (for receivers without loop-through facilities and for RF inputs to distribution amplifiers).
20 Multimeter.
21 Inclinometer.
22 Compass.
23 Signal strength meter.
24 Digging tools (where appropriate).
25 Torch or inspection lamp (for working in attic spaces).

Wall mounting

The most common mounting medium is brickwork, in which the compressive strength can vary from 7 N/mm^2 to 70 N/mm^2. In addition to this, variations in mortar compositions and strengths make it very difficult to provide accurate fixing recommendations so all information provided in this chapter is given as a guide only.

The term 'static load' is used where a constant force is applied to a fixing or where known peak low frequency fluctuations are superimposed, such as in wind loading. Static loading can further be resolved into two components as shown in Figure 7.1.

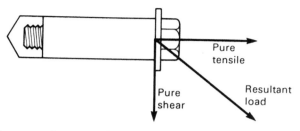

Figure 7.1   *Forces acting on wall fixings*

1   *Tensile load –* This is the load applied along the axis of the fixing and has the tendency to pull the fixing directly out from the wall. This load is sometimes referred to as the axial or pull-out force of a fixing.
2   *Shear load –* This is the force acting at right angles to the axis of the fixing. Most bolt on structures involve loads predominantly in shear although some tensile loading is present.

Although the total weight of the antenna and mounting assembly plays some part in the forces acting, the major consideration must be given to wind loading. The effects of wind loading can considerably increase the forces acting on fixings so an additional safety margin should be included to take this into account. Calculation of wind loading effects are complicated, but generally, for small antennae under 90 cm, a wind loading margin of ($\times$ 10) per fixing is normally sufficient to estimate a peak working load.

Screws and plastic wallplugs

Most wall mounting brackets, for small antennae under 90 cm, have four or five fixing points. There are many different fixing methods that can be used, but the cheapest involves screws and plastic wallplugs. This method should always be used in preference to expansion type anchors in low density blocks such as breeze. Use good quality plugs that are either made of nylon, polypropylene, or polyamide as these do not deteriorate with age. The associated screws and washers should be corrosion resistant, either plated or stainless steel. Do not use ordinary wood screws as these will rapidly corrode in exterior environments.

Pull-out loads (plastic plugs)

Fixings of this type predominantly rely on friction between the plug and mounting material for their strength. The tendency for a screw and

Table 7.2 *Rawlplug data*

Types and sizes: boxes of 1000 fixings

Product description	Presentation	Pack contents	Screw sizes	Plug length mm	Drill size mm	Cat. no
Yellow 'Hundreds'	uncarded	10 clips	Nos. 4,6	25	5	**67–125**
	carded	of 100	8,10	(1″)		**67–126**
'Twenties'	uncarded	50 panels of 20	3–5 mm			**67–128**
Red 'Hundreds'	uncarded	10 clips	Nos. 6, 8	35	6 or 6.5*	**67–130**
	carded	of 100	10, 12	(1⅜″)		**67–134**
'Twenties'	uncarded	50 panels of 20	3.3–5.5 mm			**67–138**
Brown 'Hundreds'	uncarded	10 clips	Nos. 10,	45	7	**67–231**
	carded	of 100	12,14	(1¾″)		**67–233**
'Twenties'	uncarded	50 panels of 20	5–6 mm			**67–237**

6.5 mm drill for No. 12 (5.5 mm) screw

Trade packs

Product description	Presentation	Pack contents	Screw sizes	Plug length mm	Drill size mm	Cat. no
Yellow Trade pack 300 Rawlplugs	Shrink film pack	3 clips of 100	Nos. 4, 6 8, 10 3–5 mm	25 (1″)	5	**67–900**
Red Trade pack 300 Rawlplugs	Shrink film pack	3 clips of 100	Nos. 6, 8 10, 12 3.3–5.5 mm	35 (1¾″)	6 or 6.5*	**67–902**
Brown Trade pack 300 Rawlplugs	Shrink film pack	3 clips of 100	Nos 10, 12 14 5–6 mm	45 (1¾″)	7	**67–904**

6.5 mm drill for No. 12 (5.5 mm) screw

Performance data Rawlplug

Rawlplug type	Screw size (no.)	4	6	8	10	12	14
				Pull-out loads kN			
Yellow		0.75	1.25	3.25	3.25	–	–
Red		–	1.5	2.5	4	4	–
Brown		–	–	–	3	4.75	4.75

Results obtained in common brick (1760 kg/m³) after fixing a standard wood screw to full penetration depth
Source: The Rawlplug Company

plastic plug to be pulled directly out of a material is often termed the 'axial' or 'pull out' load. Assuming zero wind speed an estimate of the axial load, per fixing, is given by the following equation:

$$\text{Axial load} = 9.81 \times \frac{\text{Weight of dish and mount}}{\text{No. of fixings}} \text{Newtons (N)}$$

(9.81 is the acceleration due to gravity (9.81 m/s^{-2}))

Allowing a wind load margin of ($\times$ 10) per fixing, we arrive at a rule of thumb estimate for the peak working load:

$$\text{Peak working load} = 100 \times \frac{\text{Weight of dish and mount}}{\text{No. of fixings}} \text{N}$$

This is still not the end of the story, a further safety factor of 3 to 5 is needed to allow a general safety margin between working load and failure load; thus the equation for minimum pull-out load is approximately given by:

$$\text{Minimum pull-out load} = 500 \times \frac{\text{Weight of dish and mount}}{\text{No. of fixings}} \text{N}$$

Practical example

Suppose the total weight of a dish, head unit and mounting bracket is 14 kg and the wall bracket has four fixing points. Using the above equation we can estimate the minimum pull-out force per fixing needed to safely secure the assembly.

$$\text{Minimum pull-out force} = 500 \times \frac{14}{4} \text{N}$$

$$= 1750 \text{ N or } 1.75 \text{ kN}$$

Therefore, a fixing with a pull-out value of at least 1.75 kN per fixing is needed. If you choose a higher value, all the better. Some manufacturers give a guide to the pull-out values of their plastic plug fixings. Table 7.2 shows the details for the 'Rawlplug' series of screw fixings. From the performance data, a correct combination of plug, screw and drill bit size can be found.

Shear loads and plastic plug fixings

Some manufacturers do not supply pull-out loads, which are essentially failure loads, for their plastic plugs. Instead, they give recommended working loads in tension and shear. The failure load is usually taken to be

Table 7.3   *Hilti HUD anchor data*

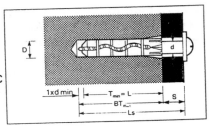

Advantages: No turning in hole
  Smooth surface maximizes friction grip
  Can be used for in-place fastenings
Material: Polyamide PA6
  Working temperature range: $-40\,°C$ to $+80\,°C$
  Setting temperature range: $-10\,°C$ to $+40\,°C$
  Screw:UTS $= 400$ N/mm^2
          YS $= 240$ N/mm^2

Setting details

Details		HUD 5	HUD 6	HUD 8	HUD 10	HUD 12	HUD 14
D hole diameter	(mm)	5	6	8	10	12	14
BT minimum hole depth	(mm)	35	40	55	65	80	90
T_{min} minimum depth of embedment in structural material	(mm)	25	30	40	50	60	70
L anchor length	(mm)	25	30	40	50	60	70
Ls required screw length	(mm)	29 + S	35 + S	46 + S	58 + S	70 + S	82 + S
d required screw shank diameter	(mm)	2.5–4	4.5–5	5–6	7–8	8–10	10–12
d required screw number		4–7	9–10	10–14	16–18	18–24	24–32

Working loads in tension (Zwl) and shear (Qwl) (factor of safety $= 5$)

Base material			HUD 5	HUD 6	HUD 8	HUD 10	HUD 12	HUD 14
Concrete	$\beta w = 35$ N/mm^2	Zwl(kN)	0.30	0.55	0.85	1.40	2.00	3.00
		Qwl (kN)	0.40	0.90	1.25	2.20	3.00	5.60
Sand-lime block*	$\beta w = 45$ N/mm^2	Zwl (kN)	0.20	0.40	0.70	1.00	–	–
		Qwl (kN)	0.25	0.56	0.74	1.32	–	–
Solid fired brick*	$\beta w = 47$ N/mm^2	Zwl (kN)	0.17	0.35	0.55	–	–	–
		Qwl (kN)	0.24	0.30	0.44	–	–	–
Aerated concrete*	$\beta w = 7.5$ N/mm^2	Zwl (kN)	0.09	0.15	0.20	–	–	–
		Qwl (kN)	0.13	0.18	0.30	–	–	–
Aerated concrete*	$\beta = 2.5$ N/mm^2	Zwl (kN)	0.02	0.03	0.06	–	–	–
		Qwl (kN)	0.04	0.05	0.08	–	–	–

* For brickwork and masonry, specific performance data cannot be assured owing to the wide diversity and variety of these materials. The loads given above must therefore be regarded as guide values only. For critical applications, load tests should be carried out. Please contact our Technical Advisory Service for further details.
Source: Hilti (GB) Ltd.

five times greater than this by applying a general safety factor. As mentioned above most bracket fixings have loads predominantly in shear, although some tensile loading is present particularly on the upper fixings. An estimate of shear load, assuming no wind loading is given by:

$$\text{Shear load} = 9.81 \times \frac{\text{Weight of antenna} + \text{bracket}}{\text{Number of fixings}} \, \text{N}$$

Again, if we allow a wind load margin of ($\times 10$) per fixing for small antennae, we arrive at the following rule of thumb equation for the peak working load in shear:

$$\text{Shear working load} = 100 \times \frac{\text{Weight of antenna} + \text{bracket}}{\text{Number of fixings}} \, \text{N}$$

Practical example

Using the previous example of a 14 kg antenna and mounting bracket and four fixing points, the shear working load would be:

$$\text{Shear working load} = 100 \times \frac{14}{4}$$

$$= 350 \, \text{N or } 0.35 \, \text{kN}$$

To provide a sound fixing, a working shear value of at least 0.35 kN is needed. Table 7.3 shows the drill size, fixing and working loads for the Hilti HUD series of universal anchors.

Purpose designed fixings

If you do not wish to use the cheapest method of fixing, a far easier and quicker method at little extra cost can be to use the purpose designed fixing, type HRD-HS 10/10 supplied by Hilti (GB) Ltd. This fixing, for small 60/70 cm antennae, includes a polyamide anchor suitable for a variety of masonry materials and comes complete with a galvanized and yellow-chromated screw. After drilling and clearing a 10 mm diameter hole, the fixing is simply hammered in as far as it will go, and finally tightened with a 13 mm spanner. A suitable, corrosion resistant washer is needed for each fixing. The recommended maximum working load for these fixings is 0.5 kN and the failure load is 3.5 kN. Figure 7.2 illustrates the method of installation and construction of the fixing.

Expansion anchors

For larger wall mounted dishes, patio stands or pole mounted dishes using T & K wall brackets, 'Rawlbolt' expansion anchors are the ideal

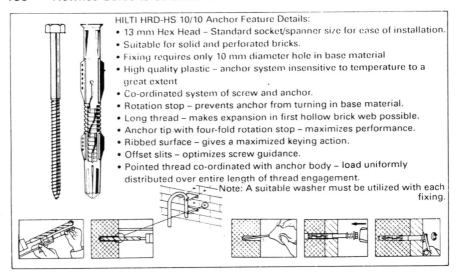

HILTI HRD-HS 10/10 Anchor Feature Details:
- 13 mm Hex Head – Standard socket/spanner size for ease of installation.
- Suitable for solid and perforated bricks.
- Fixing requires only 10 mm diameter hole in base material
- High quality plastic – anchor system insensitive to temperature to a great extent
- Co-ordinated system of screw and anchor.
- Rotation stop – prevents anchor from turning in base material.
- Long thread – makes expansion in first hollow brick web possible.
- Anchor tip with four-fold rotation stop – maximizes performance.
- Ribbed surface – gives a maximized keying action.
- Offset slits – optimizes screw guidance.
- Pointed thread co-ordinated with anchor body – load uniformly distributed over entire length of thread engagement.

Note: A suitable washer must be utilized with each fixing.

Figure 7.2   *HRD-HS 10/10 fixing (Source: HILTI (GB) Ltd)*

fixing (see Figure 7.3). M8 and M10 are typical sizes used in brickwork and sizes of M12 or above are used for patio stands bolted to concrete paving slabs. These fixings are plated to withstand corrosion and provide one of the most secure fixings into brickwork. As a general rule, expansion anchors above 16 mm hole size (M10 Rawlbolts) are not normally recommended for brickwork although 20 mm hole size (M12 Rawlbolts) may be used in engineering brick used in some older Victorian houses. Always try to keep as much brick round the fixing as possible and do not fix higher than four brick courses from the top of an unrestrained wall or on a

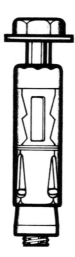

Figure 7.3   *Expanding Rawlbolt anchor*

corner brick. Expansion anchors should not be used with breeze or other low density blocks since these materials have low compressive strengths. Only plastic screw fixings or special resin bonded fixings work well with this mounting medium since the fixing method does not rely on compressive forces. A word of warning when using Rawlbolts, never overtighten because the compressive forces involved can easily crack brickwork. A torque wrench should be used and Rawlbolts should be tightened to the recommended torque shown in Table 7.4. The Rawlbolt installation method is as follows:

1 Drill holes to the recommended diameter and depth and clear the debris.
2 Insert the expansion sleeves into the holes and position the bracket.
3 Pass the bolt through the mounting bracket and into the expansion sleeves and tighten to the recommended torque.

Sleeve anchors

A cheaper alternative to expansion bolts is to use sleeve anchors such as 'Rawloks' manufactured by the Rawlplug company (see Figure 7.4). These can be used to secure wall mounting brackets in brickwork and can be fitted very quickly. Table 7.5 shows the product range and perform-ance data.

Fitting of wall mounted antennae

Some manufacturers supply a template, on the back of the flatpack, in order to drill the dish mounting holes. A slight breeze up a ladder with a large flapping piece of cardboard in one hand and a hammer drill in the other is not a pleasant scenario. Throw it away. Drill and temporarily fix one point first, put a spirit level on it, then mark out the other holes. The dish and LNB are best assembled at ground level, according to the manufacturer's instructions, and taken up the ladder, in one piece, for offering up to the mounting bracket. Be careful not to knock the feedhorn. This component is manufactured to the highest standards and any dent could render it useless. On occasions, where cement rendering masks the location of the brick courses, it is necessary to drill a small pilot hole to check the dust colour and drill resistance to locate brick rather than mortar; unfortunately a trial and error method is the only way to do this. Rendering is also used in some modern houses and extensions as a way of facing cheap breeze block construction. A small test bore will often indicate the structure of the underlying material so the appropriate fixing method can be selected.

Table 7.4   *Rawlbolt data*

Bolt size		M6	M8	M10	M12	M16	M20	M24
Shield length	mm	45	50	60	75	115	130	150

Fixing thickness loose bolt

		M6	M8	M10	M12	M16	M20	M24
Max.	mm	10 25 40	10 25 40 50	10 25 50 75	10 25 40 60	15 30 60 60	100 100	150
Min.	mm	0 0 0	0 0 0 0	0 0 0 0	0 0 0 0	0 10 30 25	60 25	100

Material

	M6	M8	M10	M12	M16	M20	M24
Electro plate Aluminium	• • • • • •	• • • • • •	• • • • • • •	• • • • • •	• • • •	—	• • •
Bronze	• •	• •	• • • •	•	• •	—	•

Fixing thickness bold projecting

		M6	M8	M10	M12	M16	M20	M24
Max.	mm	10 25 60 10		25 60 15 30	60 15 30	75 15 35 75	15 30	100 75 120
Min.	mm	0 0 0 0		0 0 0 0	0 0 0	0 0 10 35	0 10	30 0 75

Material

	M6	M8	M10	M12	M16	M20	M24
Electro plate	• • • •	• • • •	• •	• • • •	• • • •	• •	• • •

		M6	M8	M10	M12	M16	M20	M24
Hole diameter in structure	mm	12	14	16	20	25	32	38
Min. hole depth in structure	mm	50	55	65	85	125	140	160
Hole diameter in fixture	mm	6.5	9	11	13	17	22	26
Bolt tightening torque in concrete	Nm	6.5	15	27	50	120	230	400
Bolt tightening torque in 20.5 N/mm² brick	Nm	5	7.5	13.0	23.0	–	–	–

Loads for plated steel Rawlbolt with 5.8 grade bolt

Size		M6	M8	M10	M12	M16	M20	M24

Safe static load for 30 N/mm² concrete

		M6	M8	M10	M12	M16	M20	M24
Tension	kN	3.3	4.5	5.8	9.1	20.0	29.4	35.8
Shear	kN	2.1	4.4	6.1	12.4	27.6	36.4	50.0

Ultimate load 30 N/mm² concrete

		M6	M8	M10	M12	M16	M20	M24
Tension	kN	12.2	15.4	21.2	30.9	73.1	100.5	125.5
Shear	kN	7.6	16.4	24.5	40.4	86.0	131.4	165.2
Normal edge distance	mm	90	105	120	150	190	240	285
Normal spacing between bolts	mm	130	155	175	220	275	350	420

Suggested design loads for 20.5 N/mm² class 3 brick

		M6	M8	M10	M12	
Tension	kN	1.8	2.3	2.9	4.3	Bolts over M12 size
Shear	kN	1.8	2.3	2.9	4.3	are not generally recommended for

Ultimate load — use in brickwork

		M6	M8	M10	M12
Tension	kN	9.2	11.35	14.35	21.5
Normal edge distance and spacing	mm	300	300	300	300

Loads for bolt projecting and aluminium bronze Rawlbolts vary slightly from those specified. Please consult Rawlplug Technical Advisory Department for further details.
Source: The Rawlplug Company.

Cable entry holes

Cable entry holes should be a millimetre or two larger in diameter than the cable otherwise scuffing or damage to the outer sheath may result during installation. The hole should be drilled from the inside out and should have a downward tilt so that rain water will not drain into the house from outside. Large multi-sheath cables may be rolled up to feed through the appropriate hole. On completion of the installation, the hole should be sealed with a waterproof compound.

Large multi-sheath cables are best fed through walls. Thinner single coax cables can be conveniently fed through window frames, although this practice is not advisable with uPVC or metal window frames. For drilling the coax entry holes into wooden window frames a $^5/_{16}$ inch (8 mm) auger bit and hand brace does the neatest job. Angle the bit downwards and drill from the inside out to avoid splintering the wood on the inside. If a variable speed electric drill is acquired the hand brace is not needed. A stiff piece of wire is often useful to draw the cable through a cavity wall. Coax often tends to feed into the cavity if an obstruction, such as cavity wall insulation, is present. This material has an irritating habit of dropping down over the hole and blocking cable entry.

Tacking up the cable

Always agree the shortest route of the cable with the customer and try to make it as unobtrusive as possible by following natural lines of the building such as eaves or window frames; also avoid tacking cables close to entrances since small children often like to tug at them. Bending radii should be at least ten times the diameter of the cable in the absence of

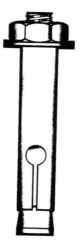

Figure 7.4   *Rawlok sleeve anchor*

Table 7.5 *Rawlok data*

Bolt size	M4.5			M6				M8						M10		M12			M16	
Anchor length mm	26	38	58	42	42 SS	66	92	48	48 SS	75	100	58	70 SS	70	98	126	64	108 142 84	114	158
Max. fixture thickness** mm	5	9	27	9	9	35	60	9	9	36	60	9	22	22	50	80	13	55 90 25	57	100
Min hole depth* mm	22	30	30		35				40					50		55			60	
Anchor hole diameter mm		6			8				10					12		16			20	
Rec. tightening torque Nm		2.5			6.0				11.0					22.0		38.0			95.0	

SS denotes stainless steel.
* Minimum recommended hole depth in concrete of 30 N/mm² compressive strength.
** Minimum hole depth for maximum fixture thickness; for thinner fixtures increase hole depth accordingly.

Loads at minimum hole depth

Size		M4.5	M6	M8	M10	M12	M16
Safe static load 30 N/mm² concrete							
Tension	kN	1.5	2.2	3.2	4.0	4.6	5.9
Shear	kN	1.8	2.5	3.4	5.4	7.8	14.5
Ultimate load 30 N/mm² concrete							
Tension	kN	5.9	8.9	12.1	16.0	17.9	22.7
Shear	kN	10.0	14.2	17.2	20.3	30.0	50.2
Minimum edge distance							
Tension	mm	60	75	80	100	110	120
Shear	mm	60	80	100	120	160	200
Min. spacing between bolts	mm	60	80	100	120	160	200
Safe static load for 20.5 N/mm² brickwork							
Tension	kN	0.6	0.9	1.2	1.6	1.9	
Shear	kN	1.4	1.5	1.6	1.7	1.9	
Ultimate load for 20.5 N/mm² brickwork							
Tension	kN	3.0	4.3	5.9	7.6	9.1	
Shear	kN	6.6	7.1	7.8	8.5	9.2	

Bolts above M12 art not suitable for brickwork

Loose bolt

Bolt size	M6		M8		M10	
Anchor length mm	45	70	55	80	60	75
Max. fixture thickness mm**	9	35	9	35	9	35
Min. hole depth* mm	35		45		55	
Anchor/hole diameter mm	8		10		12	
Rec. tightening torque Nm	6.0		11.0		22.0	

Loose bolt

Bolt size	M4.5				M6		M8	
Anchor length mm	34	58	76	98	60	86	74	102
Max. fixture thickness mm**	19	28	46	70	28	52	35	62
Min. hole depth* mm	16		30		35		40	
Anchor/hole diameter mm	6				8		10	
Rec. tightening torque Nm	2.5				6.0		11.0	

Round head

Bolt size	M4.5				M6		M8	
Anchor length mm	32	54	74	96	58	82	64	92
Max. fixture thickness mm**	16	25	45	67	25	50	25	52
Anchor/hole diameter mm	6				8		10	
Rec. tightening torque Nm	2.5				6.0		11.0	

* Minimum recommended hole depth in concrete of 30 N/mm² compressive strength.
** Minimum hole depth for maximum fixture thickness; for thinner fixtures increase hole depth accordingly.
Source: The Rawlplug Company

manufacturer's figures and the cable must not be allowed to scuff against sharp edges. Clips should be used of a size and type such that the cable is not deformed in any way; also perfectly regular tacking distances should be avoided. The recommended tacking intervals are less than 750 mm for vertical runs and less than 230 mm for horizontal runs. Fixings to poles should be less than 230 mm. For heavier multi-sheath cables the above intervals should be shorter as thought appropriate. Any extensions to cables should be done with the appropriate line connectors so that the impedance is within cable tolerance. They should also be overwrapped with self-amalgamating tape and well supported if outside. Leave a sufficient length of cable at the head end to perform all the necessary wiring and to form a drip loop. Finally form the cable into a drip loop at the point of entry so that any water droplets form at a lower level.

Where standard wall mounting is not possible

In a small number of cases a suitable wall for mounting may not be available for any one of the reasons outlined in Chapter 6. As indicated there, the solution is often a pole mounted antenna attached to the wall with a T & K bracket. A typical example is shown in Figure 7.5 where the antenna needs to be lifted above the eaves to avoid signal blockage. Two-piece T & K brackets are available in 12, 18 and 24 inch lengths to suit a range of common eave widths. The T & K bracket is bolted to the wall using M8 and M10 Rawlbolts. A four or five feet length of pole is attached to the antenna using heavy duty U-bolts. The whole assembly is then taken up the ladder and attached to the T & K bracket using heavy duty U-bolts. Unfortunately, as mentioned in Chapter 6, some manufacturer's

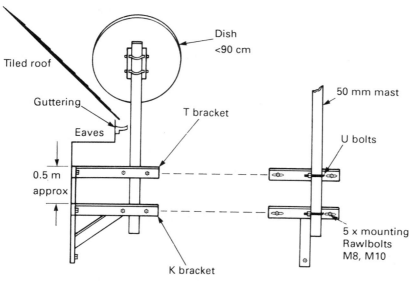

Figure 7.5 *A typical pole mount using T & K brackets*

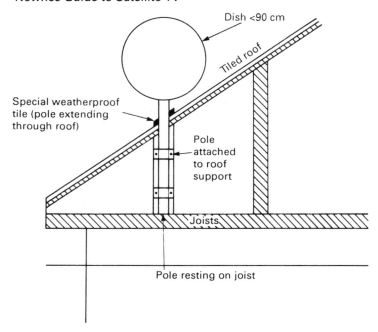

Figure 7.6 *Pole mounted in attic space*

package system antennae are unsuitable for pole mounting whilst some others have optional pole mounting kits with elevation adjustment brackets (azimuth is simply set by rotating the antenna on the pole).

Due to wind loading effects, even on a relatively small antennae of 65 cm, a pole with a thick cross-sectional wall of at least 6 mm ($\frac{1}{4}$ inch) and an outside diameter of 50 mm (2 inch) should be chosen. This may be made of galvanized steel or alloy specifically manufactured for the purpose. Poles may also be embedded in concrete for location in gardens. A typical 'planting depth' for the pole is between 0.6 and 1 m into a 0.5 m diameter concrete-filled hole. The pole itself may be filled with concrete for extra resistance to whip and bending. All poles must be set perfectly vertical by performing multiple checks with a spirit level. Nothing looks worse than a pole that is not vertical from all viewing directions.

Another method of pole mounting in awkward situations is to place the pole in the attic attached to joists and exit the pole through a tile in the roof. Special weatherproof tiles have been developed to encase the exit. The antenna is then mounted to the pole outside in the usual way. Figure 7.6 shows this little used arrangement.

Multi-satellite TVRO installations

The future and multi-satellite installations

It is envisaged that multi-satellite systems of the future will be much smaller than the present day monsters designed for low power multi-satellite reception. With the increasing number of launches of semi-DBS and DBS satellites, small polar mount antennae under 90 cm will ultimately become the top-of-the-range systems of the future. Existing broadcasters are bound to duplicate their offerings on the new generation of medium to high power satellites. It is difficult to visualize any antenna above 1 m ever taking off in a big way with the general public. Small motorized systems may be mounted on walls or poles similarly to their fixed satellite cousins.

Larger multi-satellite installations

Larger multi-satellite antennae are frequently accompanied by a tripod-like patio mount stand. These can be bolted direct using M12, or greater, Rawlbolts to three heavyweight concrete slabs, or bolted to a specially prepared concrete base (or concrete pads). The concrete slab method can also be used if the best site for the antennae is on a flat roof which cannot be directly drilled. Cables, provided they are polyethylene sheathed, may be directly buried for underground routing. The depth of burial is not critical, providing the customer is aware of the routing. The use of conduit or ducting can be advantageous for possible future cable replacement. In other cases where the installation is remote from the building, overhead spans of cable may be used. The cable needs to be supported by a galvanized, stranded steel, support wire attached to rigid eyelet wall fixings. The cable is attached to the support wire with plastic cable clips and the overall sag at the centre should be between 1.5 and 2.5 per cent of the span length.

Earthing of metalwork

The premature failure of RF input stages in LNBs and tuner units is often attributed to a static electricity build up in the antenna. This can be discharged by earthing the antenna metalwork to a nearby earthing point such as an attic water pipe. In the absence of a suitable earthing point, connection to a grounding rod, buried at the foot of the antenna may be the solution. A conductor of minimum diameter 1.5 mm should be used for the purpose. Earthing of metalwork does not offer protection against lightning however, this can destroy the LNB whether earthed or not.

Assembly of antenna and head units

Most antennae arrive in flat packs and need to be assembled along with their mounting brackets. This is a fairly straightforward process since comprehensive instructions are included. Screwdrivers, molegrips and a set of ring spanners are the only tools normally needed to complete the

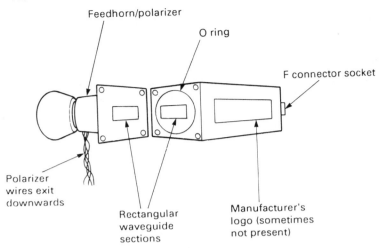

Figure 7.7 *Orientation of feedhorn and LNB assembly*

assembly. The head units of some single satellite systems are often prefabricated in one piece but others consist of a feedhorn/magnetic polarizer assembly and LNB which need to be bolted together with an 'O' ring seal between them to prevent moisture ingress. The exit wire or wires for the polarizer embedded in the feedhorn usually exit downwards and indicate the orientation of the feedhorn relative to the ground. A logo, when present, similarly provides a clue to the correct LNB orientation relative to the ground. Another clue is the resonant probe in the LNB throat, it is usually vertical. Feedhorn/polarizers with a rectangular waveguide must be matched dimension to dimension with the associated waveguide section in the LNB as shown in Figure 7.7.

Some head units consist of three components, a separate feedhorn, polarizer and LNB. The component parts all need to be bolted together using 'O' ring seals, again with attention to the alignment of the waveguide bores. Both these types often have a transition from a circular waveguide to a rectangular waveguide within the feedhorn or polarizer section.

8 Installation: antenna alignment and wiring

Instrumentation

Although it is possible to align an antenna by trial and error for DIY purposes, a considerable saving in time and energy can be gained by the use of specialist instruments. This chapter is a guide to the availability and use of such instruments along with the necessary wiring details for various systems. Courses of action are also outlined for DIY installation with no instruments.

Compass and inclinometer

A compass is an essential instrument used in both site survey work and antenna alignment. The cheap Christmas cracker variety is definitely out for professional work but may be used for one off DIY. A good sighting compass includes mirror, sighting lines and 360° bearing graduations and can be purchased from camping/sports shops. An inclinometer is essential for the measurement of elevation but some manufacturers stamp elevation scales on their mounting brackets for simple AZ/EL mounts. However, these are not too accurate unless the wall to which the dish is mounted is truly vertical. With offset focus dishes care must be exercised in the use of inclinometers since the offset angle needs to be taken into account. A temporary inclinometer, for DIY, can be made from a cheap protractor, piece of wood, nail and a plumb line.

Wideband 1st IF signal strength meters

A satellite signal strength meter is a boon to optimizing picture quality. A simple, peak level signal strength meter can be obtained for just a few tens of pounds. The cheapest units are simply connected in series with the LNB/receiver coax using F connectors and are thus powered by the LNB voltage feed. The first IF output from the LNB at approximately 950 MHz to 1750 MHz is monitored. The major disadvantage of this type is that the absolute signal level cannot be measured for comparison on each installation. They are simple peak meters which constantly need re-setting as the needle reaches full scale. More elaborate peak signal strength meters, costing a few hundreds of pounds, enable signal levels to be measured and compared by incorporating a multi-switched sensitivity facility. The final switch position and the meter reading combine to give an absolute indication of the received signal strength from each polarization sense. A further advantage of this type is that they power up the LNB using internal batteries, so only one connection is needed to the meter.

Selective signal strength meters

The ultimate signal strength meter is one which measures individual channel signals within the satellite 1st IF band. These portable instruments are expensive and elaborate and may incorporate the following features:

1 Selectable signal level measurement in dBμV.
2 Measurement of C/N ratio for each channel.
3 Direct channel or frequency input.
4 Composite video output.
5 Audio output and built-in loadspeaker allowing control of tone subcarriers between 5 and 8 MHz.
6 Remote feed of LNB via internal rechargeable batteries.
7 Microcomputer system control.

Spectrum analysers

These instruments are considered the 'Rolls Royce' of signal strength monitoring and can be expensive (often in excess of two thousand pounds). They basically plot a graph of frequency verses signal power over the satellite 1st IF range 950 MHz to 1750 MHz. The horizontal axis represents frequency and the vertical axis represents signal power. With this type of display, all a satellite's channels having the same polarization sense can be seen at a glance in the form of individual peaks. For portability the units are battery powered and often have a liquid crystal display screen rather than a cathode ray tube. These are invaluable for optimizing cross-polar rejection since individual channel signal level is the best cue to optimizing the skew setting of linear polarized signals.

Outdoor cable connections (fixed satellite systems)

There appears to be no standardization with regard to cable requirements for various manufacturer's dishes. Some use single coax where the 1st IF signals are fed down the cable from the dish and a d.c. voltage is fed back up the cable from the receiver to supply the LNB. This d.c. voltage can be level varied to switch the solid state V/H switch type of polarizer. Other manufacturers use coax with an additional polarizer lead to alter the polarization sense of a magnetic polarizer. The LNB supply of 15 V is fed up the coax and an additional cable is used to feed current to the polarizer. This current is approximately 0 mA for vertical polarization and 40 to 80 mA for horizontal polarization. The current return is via the coax braid. The outdoor connection to the polarizer can be effected with a single section of connector strip or a 'Skotch lock' which on completion is overwrapped with self-amalgamating tape to prevent corrosion due to moisture ingress. Another often-used configuration uses coax with two separate polarizer leads. These magnetic polarizers use twin direction current flow, -40 mA and $+40$ mA approx, to select the polarization sense. Again two sections of common connector strip or a pair of Skotch locks can be used to provide the electrical connections. Remember to overwrap with self-amalgamating tape.

The coaxial cable/LNB connection is simply made with an F-connector. The twist-on variety are the simplest to fit. Leave sufficient cable to form a drop loop so that any water will drip from the lowest point, away from the connection itself. A weather-proof rubber boot or self-amalgamating tape should be used to finally seal the connection from the environment. Of the two, self-amalgamating tape is preferred since some makes of rubber boot can perish and crack with time.

Alignment of a fixed satellite antenna

Alignment of AZ/EL mounts is fairly easy and normally takes only a few minutes to perform. In central footprint areas the signal is so strong that slight misalignment is not noticeable. However, in fringe areas, between differing recommended dish sizes, alignment can be somewhat more critical and time consuming. For example, Astra 1A downlinks four separate beams with varying footprint coverage. To receive all sixteen possible channels, with adequate signal strength, requires absolutely spot-on alignment in fringe areas. The procedure for alignment, assuming a budget wideband peak signal strength meter is to hand, is described below. If a signal strength meter is not available, such as in DIY installation, then set up a TV outside to monitor the signal or get someone to shout up with 'better or worse' feedback. In order to help with DIY installation, some satellite receivers come conveniently equipped with an AGC voltage output point, the level of which drops as the signal level increases. A temporary wire can be run up to the antenna and the AGC voltage monitored as it is adjusted. A general purpose low cost multimeter is sufficient for this. Another method adopted for DIY installation is the inclusion of an audio oscillator in the satellite receiver which, when connected to a TV with the volume turned up to a suitable level, produces an audible tone that increases in pitch with signal strength.

Alignment method

1 Switch off the receiver to disable the 15–24 V LNB feed. Any temporary shorts in the cable connections can blow internal fuses in the receiver!

2 Stand directly below the dish with a sighting compass and note some landmark, such as a roof apex or tree, at the required magnetic bearing.

3 Connect the LNB output to the 'in' port of the signal strength meter with an additional length of coaxial cable. Connect the main coaxial cable (connected to the receiver) to the 'out' port.

4 Switch the receiver on. An optional check for shorts with a multimeter is a good plóy before switching on.

5 Tighten all the elevation and azimuth adjusters. Take up any slack but do not tighten so much that the dish cannot be moved with moderate effort.

6 Set the elevation adjuster using either the manufacturer's stamped graduations or an inclinometer. A ruler will be needed to set this on some makes of antenna.

7 Climb up the ladder and sight the boom to the chosen landmark.

8 Signals from the targeted satellite should now be detected. If not swing the dish a few degrees either way in azimuth until an indication is detected.

9 Trim the elevation and azimuth adjustments for maximum signal strength.

10 Some systems, without programmable linear polarization settings, need a physical skew adjustment. This is performed by simply rotating the feedhorn/LNB assembly in its holder by the appropriate amount given in the manufacturer's instructions. This procedure is not necessary with circular polarization used on DBS satellites.

11 Finally, fully tighten the adjusters, thread the coax through the boom, form a drip loop, and refit the F connector ensuring that there are no sharp kinks in the cable.

12 Check the received picture quality, and if satisfactory overwrap the whole LNB F-connection with self-amalgamating tape or a weatherproof boot.

13 Mark or scratch lines on the adjusters so that realignment of the dish is made easy if wind moves the dish at a later date.

Outdoor cable connections (multi-satellite systems)

The cabling requirements of multi-satellite motorized systems are significantly more complex. The electrical connections are as follows:

Actuator motor power: Two heavy gauge wires for +36 V motor power.

Actuator position sensor: Three light gauge wires for +5 V, ground, and count pulses.

Polarizer: One, two, or three light gauge wires depending on type fitted. For motor driven polarizers, +5 V, ground and pulse. For magnetic polarizers one, or more commonly two, wires are needed

LNB feed and signal out: Coaxial cable.

There seems to be no universal colour code for multi-satellite wiring so Figure 8.1 shows a suggested outdoor wiring scheme using cable type K1005 from Volex Radex. It is important to stick rigidly to the same colour coding for each installation otherwise confusion and mistakes may occur. Pay particular attention to the actuator motor power connections since mistakes here may cause considerable damage due to the relatively high voltage and current involved. The information contained in the particular manufacture's installation manual should be read carefully before any wiring is attempted.

Any connections left exposed to the environment should be over-wrapped with self-amalgamating tape and rain drip loops formed to drain water away from them. The corresponding indoor connections to the positioner unit will be dealt with in Chapter 9.

Alignment of a polar mount antenna

The alignment of a polar mount antenna is considerably more fiddly than simple AZ/EL mounts since accurate tracking of the whole visible geo-arc is needed by one simple movement around the polar axis. Both polar mount, and the more popular derivative called the modified polar mount, geometry were discussed in detail in Chapter 2. Once set up, it can be either hand operated or motor driven by remote control. The point where

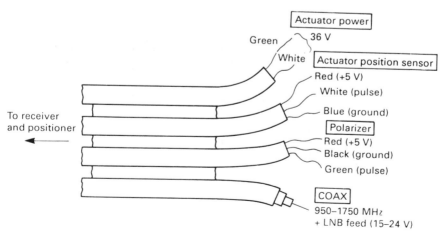

Figure 8.1 *Suggested wiring details for cable type K1005*

Table 8.1   *Modified polar mount angles for various latitudes*

Latitude	Polar axis angle	Polar elevation angle	Declination angle	Apex axis angle	Apex elevation angle
0.00	0.00	90.00	0.00	0.00	90.00
0.50	0.51	89.49	0.08	0.59	89.41
1.00	1.02	88.98	0.16	1.18	88.82
1.50	1.53	88.47	0.24	1.77	88.23
2.00	2.04	87.96	0.32	2.36	87.64
2.50	2.55	87.45	0.39	2.95	87.05
3.00	3.06	86.93	0.47	3.53	86.47
3.50	3.58	86.42	0.54	4.12	85.88
4.00	4.09	85.91	0.62	4.71	85.29
4.50	4.60	85.39	0.70	5.30	84.70
5.00	5.12	84.88	0.77	5.89	84.11
5.50	5.63	84.37	0.85	6.48	83.52
6.00	6.14	83.86	0.93	7.07	82.93
6.50	6.65	83.35	1.00	7.65	82.35
7.00	7.16	82.84	1.08	8.24	81.76
7.50	7.67	82.33	1.16	8.83	81.17
8.00	8.18	81.81	1.23	9.42	80.58
8.50	8.69	81.30	1.31	10.01	79.99
9.00	9.20	80.79	1.39	10.59	79.41
9.50	9.71	80.29	1.47	11.18	78.82
10.00	10.23	79.77	1.54	11.77	78.23
10.50	10.74	79.25	1.61	12.35	77.65
11.00	11.26	78.74	1.69	12.94	77.06
11.50	11.76	78.23	1.76	13.53	76.47
12.00	12.28	77.72	1.84	14.11	75.89
12.50	12.78	77.21	1.91	14.70	75.30
13.00	13.29	76.70	1.99	15.28	74.72
13.50	13.80	76.20	2.06	15.87	74.13
14.00	14.31	75.68	2.14	16.45	73.55
14.50	14.82	75.17	2.21	17.04	72.96
15.00	15.33	74.67	2.29	17.62	72.38
15.50	15.84	74.16	2.37	18.21	71.79
16.00	16.35	73.64	2.44	18.79	71.21
16.50	16.86	73.13	2.51	19.38	70.62
17.00	17.37	72.62	2.58	19.96	70.04
17.50	17.88	72.12	2.66	20.54	69.46
18.00	18.39	71.61	2.73	21.12	68.88
18.50	18.90	71.10	2.81	21.71	68.29
19.00	19.41	70.59	2.88	22.29	67.71
19.50	19.92	70.08	2.95	22.87	67.13
20.00	20.43	69.57	3.02	23.45	66.55
20.50	20.94	69.06	3.09	24.03	65.97
21.00	21.44	68.55	3.17	24.61	65.39
21.50	21.95	68.05	3.24	25.19	64.81
22.00	22.46	67.54	3.31	25.77	64.23
22.50	22.97	67.03	3.38	26.35	63.65
23.00	23.47	66.52	3.45	26.93	63.07
23.50	23.98	66.01	3.52	27.50	62.50
24.00	24.49	65.51	3.59	28.08	61.92
24.50	25.00	65.00	3.66	28.66	61.34
25.00	25.51	64.49	3.73	29.24	60.76
25.50	26.02	63.98	3.79	29.81	60.19
26.00	26.52	63.47	3.86	30.39	59.61
26.50	27.04	62.96	3.93	30.96	59.04

Table 8.1   *continued*

Latitude	Polar axis angle	Polar elevation angle	Declination angle	Apex axis angle	Apex elevation angle
27.00	27.54	62.46	4.00	31.54	58.46
27.50	28.04	61.95	4.06	32.11	57.89
28.00	28.55	61.45	4.13	32.68	57.32
28.50	29.05	60.95	4.20	33.26	56.74
29.00	29.56	60.44	4.27	33.83	56.17
29.50	30.07	59.93	4.34	34.40	55.60
30.00	30.57	59.43	4.40	34.97	55.03
30.50	31.07	58.92	4.47	35.54	54.46
31.00	31.58	58.42	4.53	36.11	53.89
31.50	32.08	57.91	4.60	36.68	53.32
32.00	32.59	57.41	4.66	37.25	52.75
32.50	33.09	56.90	4.72	37.82	52.18
33.00	33.61	56.39	4.78	38.39	51.61
33.50	34.11	55.89	4.85	38.96	51.04
34.00	34.61	55.38	4.91	39.52	50.48
34.50	35.12	54.88	4.97	40.09	49.91
35.00	35.62	54.38	5.03	40.65	49.35
35.50	36.12	53.88	5.09	41.22	48.78
36.00	36.63	53.37	5.15	41.78	48.22
36.50	37.13	52.87	5.21	42.35	47.65
37.00	37.64	52.36	5.27	42.91	47.09
37.50	38.14	51.86	5.33	43.47	46.53
38.00	38.64	51.35	5.39	44.03	45.97
38.50	39.15	50.85	5.45	44.59	45.41
39.00	39.65	50.35	5.50	45.15	44.85
39.50	40.15	49.85	5.56	45.71	44.29
40.00	40.65	49.35	5.62	46.27	43.73
40.50	41.15	48.84	5.68	46.83	43.17
41.00	41.66	48.34	5.73	47.39	42.61
41.50	42.16	47.84	5.79	47.95	42.05
42.00	42.66	47.34	5.84	48.50	41.50
42.50	43.16	46.84	5.90	49.06	40.94
43.00	43.66	46.34	5.95	49.61	40.39
43.50	44.16	45.84	6.01	50.17	39.83
44.00	44.66	45.34	6.06	50.72	39.28
44.50	45.16	44.84	6.11	51.27	38.73
45.00	45.66	44.34	6.17	51.83	38.17
45.50	46.16	43.84	6.22	52.38	37.62
46.00	46.66	43.34	6.27	52.93	37.07
46.50	47.16	42.84	6.32	53.48	36.52
47.00	47.65	42.34	6.37	54.03	35.97
47.50	48.15	41.84	6.42	54.58	35.42
48.00	48.65	41.35	6.47	55.13	34.87
48.50	49.15	40.85	6.52	55.67	34.33
49.00	49.65	40.35	6.57	56.22	33.78
49.50	50.15	39.85	6.62	56.77	33.23
50.00	50.64	39.36	6.67	57.31	32.69
50.50	51.14	38.86	6.72	57.86	32.14
51.00	51.63	38.36	6.76	58.40	31.60
51.50	52.13	37.87	6.81	58.94	31.06
52.00	52.63	37.37	6.85	59.48	30.52
52.50	53.12	36.88	6.90	60.03	29.97
53.00	53.62	36.38	6.95	60.57	29.43
53.50	54.12	35.88	6.99	61.11	28.89

Table 8.1   *continued*

Latitude	Polar axis angle	Polar elevation angle	Declination angle	Apex axis angle	Apex elevation angle
54.00	54.62	35.38	7.03	61.65	28.35
54.50	55.12	34.88	7.07	62.19	27.81
55.00	55.61	34.39	7.11	62.72	27.28
55.50	56.10	33.89	7.16	63.26	26.74
56.00	56.60	33.40	7.20	63.80	26.20
56.50	57.10	32.90	7.24	64.33	25.67
57.00	57.59	32.40	7.27	64.87	25.13
57.50	58.09	31.91	7.31	65.40	24.60
58.00	58.58	31.41	7.35	65.94	24.06
58.50	59.08	30.92	7.39	66.47	23.53
59.00	59.58	30.42	7.43	67.00	23.00
59.50	60.07	29.93	7.46	67.53	22.47
60.00	60.56	29.44	7.50	68.06	21.94
60.50	61.05	28.95	7.54	68.59	21.41
61.00	61.54	28.45	7.58	69.12	20.88
61.50	62.04	27.96	7.61	69.65	20.35
62.00	62.53	27.47	7.65	70.18	19.82
62.50	63.03	26.97	7.68	70.70	19.30
63.00	63.52	26.48	7.71	71.23	18.77
63.50	64.01	25.99	7.75	71.76	18.24
64.00	64.50	25.49	7.78	72.28	17.72
64.50	65.00	25.00	7.81	72.81	17.19
65.00	65.49	24.51	7.84	73.33	16.67
65.50	65.98	24.02	7.87	73.85	16.15
66.00	66.48	23.52	7.90	74.37	15.63
66.50	66.97	23.05	7.92	74.89	15.11
67.00	67.46	22.54	7.95	75.41	14.59
67.50	67.95	22.05	7.98	75.93	14.07
68.00	68.44	21.56	8.01	76.45	13.55
68.50	68.93	21.06	8.04	76.97	13.03
69.00	69.42	20.58	8.06	77.49	12.51
69.50	69.92	20.08	8.09	78.01	11.99
70.00	70.41	19.59	8.11	78.52	11.48
70.50	70.90	19.10	8.14	79.04	10.96
71.00	71.39	18.60	8.16	79.55	10.45
71.50	71.88	18.11	8.18	80.07	9.93
72.00	72.37	17.62	8.20	80.58	9.42
72.50	72.87	17.13	8.22	81.09	8.91
73.00	73.35	16.64	8.25	81.60	8.40
73.50	73.85	16.16	8.27	82.11	7.89
74.00	74.33	15.66	8.29	82.62	7.38
74.50	74.82	15.17	8.31	83.13	6.87
75.00	75.32	14.68	8.32	83.64	6.36
75.50	75.80	14.19	8.35	84.15	5.85
76.00	76.29	13.70	8.36	84.66	5.34
76.50	76.79	13.21	8.38	85.17	4.83
77.00	77.28	12.72	8.40	85.67	4.33
77.50	77.76	12.23	8.41	86.18	3.82
78.00	78.25	11.74	8.43	86.68	3.32
78.50	78.74	11.26	8.44	87.19	2.81
79.00	79.24	10.76	8.45	87.69	2.31
79.50	79.73	10.27	8.46	88.19	1.81
80.00	80.22	9.78	8.47	88.69	1.31
80.50	80.71	9.29	8.49	89.20	0.80
81.00	81.20	8.80	8.50	89.70	0.30

the antenna's maximum or apex elevation is achieved should correspond to a true north/south line. At this central point the antenna is said to be in its apex position, and can be driven by an equal amount either eastward or westward thus accurately tracking the geo-arc. Table 8.1 shows the modified polar mount angles, over a wide range of latitudes, and are the elevation angles set when the antenna is in its apex position.

There are many different ways of tackling the alignment of a polar mount but one requirement that they all have in common is accurate setting of the dish north/south orientation in the apex position. Unless this is found very accurately the whole geo-arc tracking process becomes a failure. The apex setting can be thought of as the setting the dish would need for receiving signals from a hypothetical satellite due south of the receiving site, this corresponds to the highest point (apex) of the geo-arc. In general, the following rules are applied and should be remembered throughout the adjustment procedure.

1 Adjust the polar elevation angle to peak signals from satellites located at or near the geo-arc's apex. That is to say, the most southerly satellites.
2 Rotate the whole mount assembly around its mast or pillar when peaking signals from satellites far from the geo-arc's apex. That is to say trimming the north/south orientation.

One widely used alignment method which seems to work satisfactorily is described in the following section.

Alignment method

1 The mounting pole must be perfectly vertical. Failure to ensure this may lead to the odd heart attack or swearing session as the adjustments progress. It is rather like the art of glasshouse erection, if the base is not level problems occur at a later stage (when putting the glass in). Set the dish to its apex position and rotate it round the mast to face as near due south as possible. A magnetically corrected sighting compass will help here. Ensure that the dish is still held in its apex position at this point. Set the polarizer reference plane so that it is not skewed in the apex position, the control leads are a visual cue, they normally exit vertically downwards if assembled correctly.
2 Obtain the latitude of the receiving site from a local ordnance survey map, and look up the relevant angles for polar elevation and apex elevation from Table 8.1 For example, if your latitude is 53.5° N the angles will be 35.88° and 28.89° respectively. From Table 8.1 a simple relationship is seen between the polar elevation angle and the apex elevation angle which is as follows:

Polar elevation angle = Apex elevation angle – Declination angle

or

Polar axis angle = Apex axis angle – Declination angle

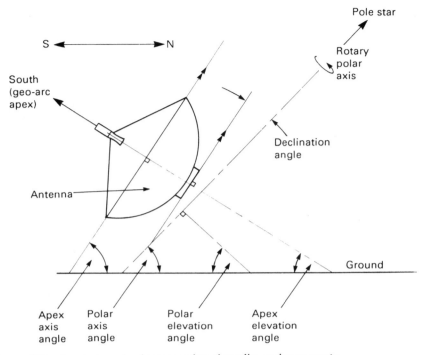

Figure 8.2 *Angle terminology used to describe polar mounts*

Therefore, if the polar elevation angle is set, followed by the apex elevation angle, the correct declination angle will automatically be set correctly. (The declination angle is relatively small and can be difficult to measure in practice.) Alternatively, the polar axis angle can be set followed by the apex axis angle. The above relationships can be understood more clearly by examining Figure 8.2.

3 Set the polar elevation angle or the corresponding polar axis angle (from Table 8.1) whichever is the most convenient to measure. The end result is the same.

4 Set the apex elevation angle or the corresponding apex axis angle (from Table 8.1) whichever is the most convenient to measure. With offset focus antennae a special measuring point is usually provided. Read the manufacturer's instructions carefully.

5 Connect up a signal strength meter to monitor the LNB output in the range 950 MHz to 1750 MHz

6 Compute, or look up from your records, the local elevation angle of a convenient satellite, as far away as possible from the geo-arc apex and call this SAT 1. At the time of writing, Intellsat VA F11 at 27.5° W is most often used to fulfil this criteria for UK locations although a more convenient and stronger signal may be available from a medium power satellite by the time this is read.

7   Monitoring the resultant elevation angle (the actual elevation of the dish), move the dish around the polar axis until the measured elevation matches the computed elevation angle for SAT 1. Hold this position with the actuator arm. Slowly rotate the whole assembly around the mast until maximum signal strength is detected from SAT 1. This procedure in effect trims up the true north/south orientation of the antenna in its apex position by exploiting the station keeping accuracy of SAT 1. It may be convenient to optimize the feed focal length at this stage.

8   By using the actuator or otherwise, move the antenna around the polar axis to a satellite close to the geo-arc apex and call this SAT 2. Finely trim the polar elevation for maximum signal strength from SAT 2.

9   Move the antenna back to SAT 1 and further trim for maximum signal strength by adjusting the north/south orientation as in 7.

10   Repeat steps 7 to 9 as often as needed for consistently peaked signal strength on both satellites. It may be found necessary to temporarily tighten bolts at each stage. If difficulty is experienced then start from scratch by re-setting the polar elevation and apex elevation angles from Table 8.1

11   Check the received picture quality and tracking over a number of satellites and when satisfied fully tighten and grease all adjuster bolts. Recheck signal strengths and picture quality in case final tightening has pulled the alignment out slightly. Repeat steps 7 to 9 if this is the case.

9 Installation: indoor work

Introduction

Indoor work can be as time consuming as all the other work put together. This is particularly so if the satellite receiver output is to be fed to a distribution amplifier for multi-room reception along with normal UHF TV signals. This chapter is intended to be a guide to most aspects of indoor work and covers most situations likely to be encountered in the domestic environment, such as the interconnections and tuning arrangements to be found in both older and modern ancillary equipment. It is vital to leave all equipment switched off until final wiring is completed and checked.

Polarizer connections

For many single satellite packages using simple V/H switched types of polarizer, no separate wiring is necessary because the d.c. switching voltages are fed up the coaxial cable to the outdoor head unit from the receiver. Where magnetic polarizers are employed, one or two extra wires need to be connected to the satellite receiver (some designs use the 0 volt outer coax braid as the polarizer's earth return). A few receivers, increasingly rare, are equipped to control mechanical polarizers, and have + 5 V, pulse and ground connections for that purpose. Refer to the manufacturer's manual for detailed connection data bearing in mind the polarizer type. With some models a suitable plug is provided for soldering onto the polarizer leads.

Actuator connections (multi-satellite systems)

Actuator requirements consist of two motor power cables (36 V) and three-way transducer leads (+ 5 V, pulse, and ground). These are connected either to the receiver or positioner unit (some receivers have built-in antenna positioner circuitry). It is vital that no mistakes are made with this wiring; in particular check that the motor power and position sensor connections are not crossed or permanent damage may result.

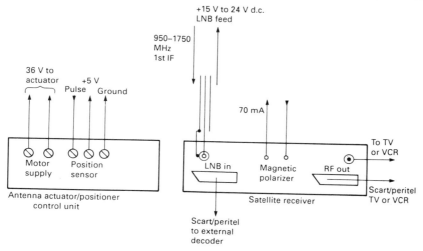

Figure 9.1   *Guide to multi-satellite receiver/positioner connections*

Figure 9.1 shows the general wiring arrangement for multi-satellite systems, but it is essential to carefully read the manufacturer's installation instructions and recheck your work before switching on and testing.

Signal interconnections

Before making any connections, ensure equipment is switched off. D.C. voltages to supply the head unit may be present even when the satellite receiver is in standby mode. Any shorts in the coaxial wiring can result in blown fuses or the destruction of special fusible safety resistors. The latter must be replaced with an identical type and not with standard resistors, to comply with current safety regulations. In my experience these are unlikely to be stocked by most dealers so extreme care must be exercised. It is wise to check for possible shorts across the coaxial cable before powering up.

Prepare the coaxial cable and fit the connector (usually an F connector) to the satellite antenna input socket. This is usually labelled 'LNB IN' or marked with a graphic dish aerial symbol. There are many possible wiring configurations used with satellite receivers, TV, and video recorders and the following is a representative sample.

RF modulator configuration (simplest method)

This method is the most basic and versatile wiring arrangement and can be used with old or modern TV sets. The RF output signal from the satellite receiver (Sat Rx) is similar to that of a transmitted terrestrial channel and a spare channel on the TV must be tuned accordingly to

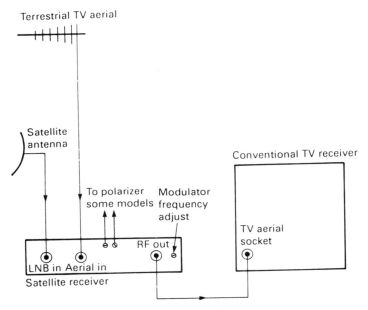

Figure 9.2   *Basic arrangement (Sat Rx and TV only)*

process the signal. In the UK, the output RF modulators are normally preset to channel 38 or 39 in the UHF band. To assist the tuning of ancillary equipment a test signal, internally generated in the satellite receiver, is usually provided. Figure 9.2 shows the basic wiring arrange-

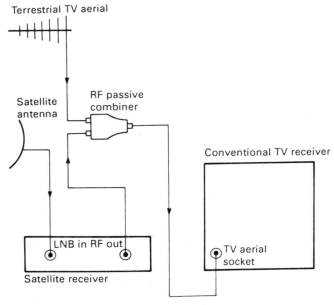

Figure 9.3   *Using a combiner where no loop-through facility exists*

ment. Most satellite receivers have a built in 'loop-through' facility which provides for the connection of an additional terrestrial UHF aerial. Where this is not present it will be necessary to use a combiner as shown in Figure 9.3.

Connecting up

1 Plug the terrestrial aerial into the appropriately labelled input socket (where fitted).
2 Connect a coaxial flylead cable (usually supplied) between the satellite receiver RF signal output socket (labelled TV/VCR or RF out) and the television receiver aerial socket.
3 A spare channel selector will need to be tuned to the satellite RF output (see later).

Including a video recorder

Figure 9.4 shows the basic RF wiring arrangement with a video cassette recorder (VCR) in circuit. It is possible to record a selected satellite channel while watching a terrestrial channel, or vice versa, although recording a satellite channel whilst watching another satellite channel is not possible at the present time with any wiring interconnection. The RF output of a VCR is normally tuned to channel 36 in the UK.

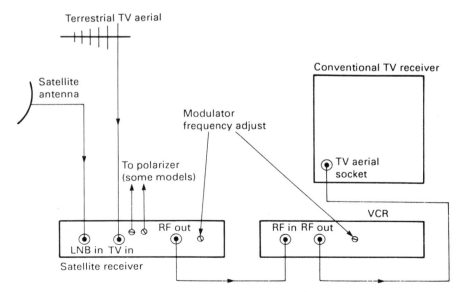

Figure 9.4 *Basic arrangement (Sat Rx, TV and VCR)*

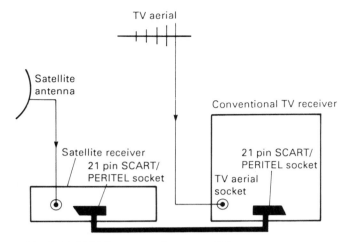

Figure 9.5   *SCART/PERITEL connections to a TV set*

Connecting up

1   Connect the terrestrial aerial into the appropriately labelled input socket.
2   Connect the RF output socket of the satellite receiver to the RF input socket of the VCR using a flylead.
3   Connect the RF output socket of the VCR to the aerial socket of the TV.
4   Switch on TV and VCR.
5   Tune a spare channel of the TV to the satellite receiver RF output.
6   Select the VCR playback channel on the TV and tune a spare VCR channel to the satellite receiver RF output. If patterning is experienced the chances are that there is a clash between the satellite receiver and VCR RF modulator frequencies. In such a case see the RF modulator adjustment section at the end of this chapter.

SCART/PERITEL alternatives

Alternative wiring arrangements using 21 pin SCART/PERITEL television connectors can provide slightly improved picture and sound quality with modern equipment by cutting out the satellite receiver RF modulator section to either the VCR or TV. Additionally, stereo sound can be utilized with suitably equipped satellite receivers and TV sets. Figure 9.5 shows the connection to a TV set which also alleviates the need for TV tuning. Satellite signals are automatically present when the auxiliary or AV channel is selected on the TV. Terrestrial TV viewing is effected by normal TV channel selection.

Figure 9.6 shows one method of interconnecting a satellite receiver,

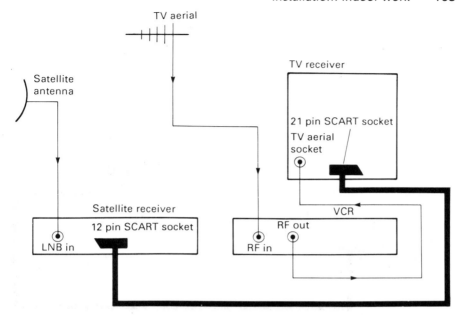

Figure 9.6 *SCART/PERITEL connections (terrestrial TV record only)*

VCR and TV using SCART/PERITEL connectors. This arrangement allows the recording of terrestrial TV whilst watching satellite TV but disallows the recording of satellite TV whilst watching terrestrial TV. Direct audio and video signals from the satellite receiver are available when the auxiliary or AV input is selected on the TV.

The foregoing limitation can be overcome by the loop-through arrangement shown in Figure 9.7. A spare VCR channel is tuned to the satellite receiver RF output for the recording of satellite programmes.

Figure 9.8 shows another method of interconnecting a satellite receiver, VCR and TV using SCART/PERITEL connectors. This configuration allows the recording of satellite TV whilst watching terrestrial TV but disallows the recording of terrestrial TV whilst watching satellite TV. The VCR must be switched to auxiliary input or AV for recording or viewing the selected satellite channel. When viewing or monitoring satellite programmes, the VCR playback channel on the TV is also selected.

The configuration shown in Figure 9.9 overcomes the previous limitation by using the RF loop-through facility to allow recording of terrestrial programmes. The VCR is switched to auxiliary input or AV only for recording satellite programmes. A spare TV channel needs tuning for the satellite receiver RF output for viewing while a terrestrial channel is being recorded. This method needs both the TV and VCR to be tuned to the satellite receiver RF output for maximum flexibility.

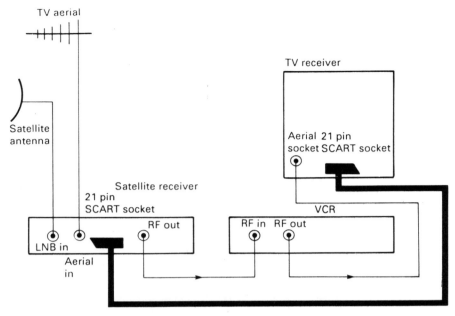

Figure 9.7 *SCART/PERITEL connections (terrestrial or satellite recording)*

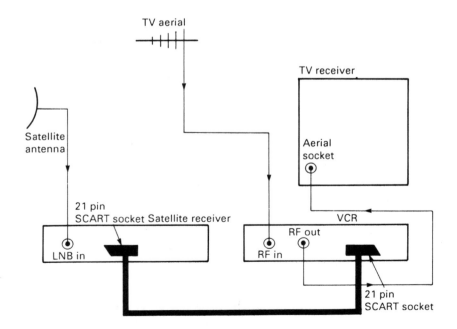

Figure 9.8 *SCART/PERITEL connections (satellite TV record only)*

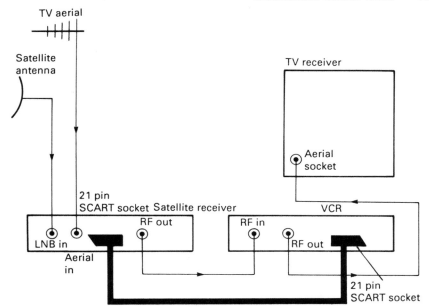

Figure 9.9 *SCART/PERITEL connections (satellite or terrestrial recording)*

Other direct audio and video connections

Many TVs and VCRs, particularly older models, do not have SCART/PERI-TEL sockets. Instead they use a combination of other sockets to provide input and output of direct audio and video signals. Video signal sockets can be BNC, Phono, PL259, or 6 pin DIN. Audio signal sockets can be Phono, 5, 6 or 7 pin DIN, and in a small number of cases a 3.5 mm jack socket. These may be specially wired to interface with a SCART socket where needed. The connection data for SCART sockets was given in Chapter 4 along with the subminiature D type socket. Figure 9.10 shows the pin numbering and connection data for the various DIN sockets likely to be encountered. The outputs from satellite receivers are all mains isolated so it is permissible to directly connect the appropriate audio outputs to the audio input of a hi-fi system.

Distribution amplifiers

UHF distribution amplifiers already exist in the lofts of many customer's houses for multi-outlet terrestrial channel viewing so it is not unreasonable to expect that the customer will want the selected channel on his/her satellite receiver to be sent to all TVs and VCRs in the residence. An extra coax cable (normal UHF quality) needs to be run up from the RF output of

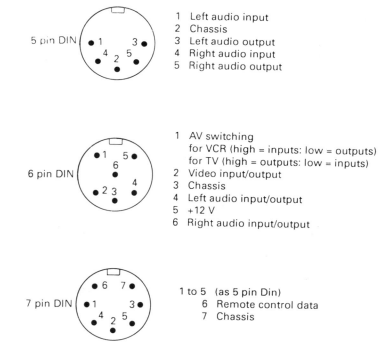

5 pin DIN
1 Left audio input
2 Chassis
3 Left audio output
4 Right audio input
5 Right audio output

6 pin DIN
1 AV switching
  for VCR (high = inputs: low = outputs)
  for TV (high = outputs: low = inputs)
2 Video input/output
3 Chassis
4 Left audio input/output
5 +12 V
6 Right audio input/output

7 pin DIN
1 to 5 (as 5 pin Din)
    6 Remote control data
    7 Chassis

Figure 9.10   *Connection data for various DIN sockets*

the satellite receiver to the input of the distribution amplifier. In addition all the TVs and VCRs will also need to be tuned to the satellite receiver RF modulator output. In view of all the extra work involved, it is wise to enquire about such a possibility at the site survey stage so an extra charge may be quoted. Much swearing and cursing often results when the dreaded words 'it's a distribution amp job' are interchanged by an unprepared installation team arriving at five o'clock in the afternoon. The prospect of crawling about in a grubby attic with 25 grams of loft in-sulation down your trousers is not one of the trade's most pleasant tasks.

The satellite receiver RF output and the terrestrial TV aerial are both connected to a standard UHF 2-way combiner/splitter which is then plugged into the aerial input of the distribution amplifier. Figure 9.11 shows the basic arrangement and from this a realization of the extra work involved will become apparent. A complication may arise, particularly in bad terrestrial TV reception areas, where a mast head amplifier is con-nected to the UHF aerial. Its 12 V power requirements are supplied via the coaxial cable from the distribution amplifier itself. If a passive combiner is used the supply voltage to it may be substantially reduced and thus the gain will dramatically fall. A simple way out of this problem is to power up the mast head amplifier from a separate 12 V supply unit (obtainable from TV aerial suppliers) and use the alternative configuration shown in Figure 9.12.

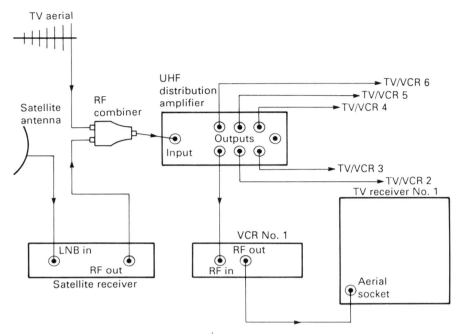

Figure 9.11   *UHF distribution amplifier with satellite channel*

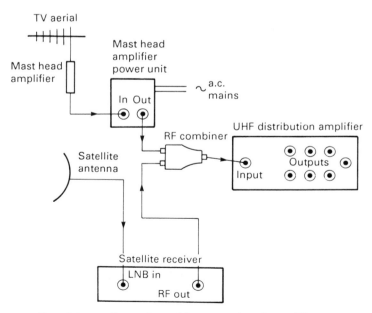

Figure 9.12   *Possible configuration with a mast head amplifier*

Tuning systems adopted with TVs and VCRs

The actual sequence of button pushing for tuning every make and model of TV and VCR that has ever been sold would necessitate the space of a few volumes. However, all the various tuning sequences can be broadly grouped into three basic types. A VHF/UHF tuner unit in a typical TV or VCR requires a specific and very stable voltage to be stored whose level corresponds uniquely to the channel tuned. In other words all modern TV and VCR tuner units employ voltage controlled tuning. The object of all currently encountered tuning systems is to store and recall on demand various tuning voltages. TV and VCR tuners incorporate variable capacitance diodes (varicaps) as part of their tuned circuits and as their reverse bias is changed the capacitance and hence the tuned frequency alters.

Preset potentiometer tuning

This is the simplest method of tuning and can be one of the easiest to use. Preset potentiometers are adjusted until the required channel is tuned. The low and high limits of the frequency range correspond to the end-stops of the potentiometers. In effect this method memorizes the tuning voltage by the position of the wiper on the resistive track. The disadvantages of this system is that moisture, dust and poor wiper contact can lead to instability and poor reproducibility of tuning voltages. Continual trimming is needed as wear progresses and reliability can be poor. This type of tuning arrangement is found on relatively old equipment but occasionally it is still adopted on budget-priced equipment. The number of potentiometers fitted varies but is usually in the range six to sixteen. Switch the AFC button (where fitted) to the OFF position while tuning and switch the AFC switch to ON when completed.

Electronic scan tuning

Electronic scan tuning is effected by storing and recalling the digital representation of a specific analogue tuning voltage level. For each numbered programme channel in turn, the tuning range is 'swept' and stops at the first channel found. Either the opportunity to store the digital representation of the tuning voltage level can be taken or the appropriate tune button pressed to restart the scan from where it left off. A variety of different methods have evolved and range from early dedicated hardware systems to modern microcomputer types which have inbuilt tuning algorithms. Some versions have an additional fine-tune option. Electronic tuning is far more reliable than the potentiometer method since no moving parts are needed and the number of available channel stores can be increased. Earlier models allowed scanning in one direction only, with a wraparound facility but modern versions allow scanning in both directions which is an advantage if you overshoot the required channel. The disadvantages of this type of tuning is the tediously long time it takes to set up initially. The current sweep position within the tuning band is often not displayed, particularly on VCRs. TV tuning is sometimes helped by the 'on screen' appearance of a horizontal bar whose instantaneous length is a measure of the sweep position within the tuning band.

Direct channel entry or frequency synthesis

The frequency synthesis system allows for direct key entry of the required channel. For example if UHF channel 38 is to be tuned, all that is needed is to open the memory, punch in the keys 38 and press the memory button within a preset time limit. This tuning method is fast to set up but a knowledge of locally received channel numbers is needed. A few TVs and VCRs of this type also have additional scan up and scan down buttons similar to the above system for fine tuning. For equipment without a numerical key pad (or remote control), channel entry is usually performed by a channel 10s button and a channel 1s button to input the tuning information, and a dual seven segment display mirrors the information keyed in. More modern equipment has a comprehensive 'on screen' display to assist tuning and other preset conditions. The procedure is repeated for each programme channel as required.

RF modulator adjustment

On occasions, particularly with RF interconnections, interference may occur due to the settings of the RF modulators on the satellite receiver and a connected VCR. This effect may be further compounded by local terrestrial TV transmitters operating in the same narrow frequency band. This can be overcome by fine tuning the modulator frequency presets which are usually located on the back panel of the equipment. The adjustments are made to minimize interference patterning between any of the contributing signals. It will be necessary to retune the TV and/or VCR after each adjustment to check the result. By trial and error, a combination of settings will be quickly arrived at. However, in some service areas this may be particularly difficult and it may be necessary to resort to direct AV connection between two items of equipment to exclude a modulator.

10 Repair of satellite equipment

Introduction

Sooner or later most domestic electronic equipment breaks down and the initial supplier or a technician is expected to perform a quick and reliable repair. Larger retail outlets are normally not interested in repairs once the equipment sold is out of guarantee. This is put into practice by pricing themselves out of the market with high call-out charges that customers are unwilling to pay. It seems that they have neither the resources nor the manpower to effect a fast and efficient repair to all the equipment they have sold. Fortunately, this leaves a large pool of repair work available to independent dealers or self-employed technicians who have much lower operating costs and can respond more quickly. However, in many cases, this may be difficult since the relevant service information is often unavailable for some time after the release of new equipment.

This chapter is intended to be a guide to the servicing of satellite receiving equipment and the treatment will be biased towards the vast majority of equipment in service in the domestic environment – namely, the fixed antenna type which targets one or a group of satellites in a single orbital slot. Practically, the only difference with multi-satellite motorized types, is the restriction to magnetic or mechanical polarizers in conjunction with additional antenna positioning circuitry. Video and audio circuitry also tends to be more complicated to comply with the variety of signal formats used in current satellite transmissions.

The repair of satellite equipment is fairly straightforward and in a lot of ways is considerably easier than TV or VCR repairs. The familiar set top receiver system can be broken down into five main areas or sections.

1 *The mechanical area* – The mounting itself, the antenna, the head unit support and the feedhorn assembly.
2 *The polarizer circuit* – The polarizer, wiring and polarization control circuitry.
3 *The actuator circuit* – The outdoor actuator unit, wiring and the associated control circuitry in the positioner or receiver. This only applies to motorized polar mount antennae.

4   *The signal path area* – The low noise block, tuner/demodulator, video and audio processing circuitry. This would include any external decoders that are fitted.

5   *The power supply area* – This is the main area where a fault is likely to be encountered.

Most service calls can be prevented, particularly in the initial stages of customer ownership, over the telephone. They invariable involve 'finger trouble' with the customer controls, leads accidentally pulled out while cleaning behind the indoor unit or 'little Johnny' twiddling the various tuning controls. However, if the customer is local, it is often quicker to call and check the system out yourself since it is virtually impossible to obtain any detailed information from some customers. Never listen to claims that 'no-one has touched it' or 'it just went off' and always check the customer control settings in a logical manner before embarking on more involved diagnosis.

Once a system is installed the customer is usually pleased or even surprised with the results initially, but after a week or two has passed, they compare the picture quality with that of terrestrial TV and become more critical. The odd sparklie or minor patterning gives rise to a moan or two and much time can be fruitlessly wasted checking the alignment of the antenna. Floods of service calls come in after a heavy rain storm due to sparklies appearing but, of course, there is nothing that can be done about it. It is important to warn customers about this possibility at the installation or sales stage so that such calls may be avoided or considerably reduced.

Fault symptoms

On a service call the first thing to do is to interrogate the customer as to the exact problem he or she is experiencing. The following is a guide to the sort of questions to be asked.

1   Is the fault always present or intermittent?
2   What are the fault symptoms and when did they first appear?
3   Did the fault get progressively worse with time?
4   Has any other technician called recently to repair or attempt to repair the equipment? (Man-made faults are the worst to find!)
5   Has there been a recent thunderstorm?
6   Can all intended satellites be received well (polar mounts only)?
7   Is picture quality poorer on some channels than others?

Once the fault symptoms are established the area or subsystem where the fault lies can be quickly isolated by a few quick and easy measurements.

Test equipment

For on-site servicing, the following test equipment is all that is necessary to locate the vast majority of faults. The last two items can be considered optional due to their expense.

Signal strength meter

A lot of information about a fault can be obtained from a signal strength meter provided it has some form of calibration. This is useful for detecting head unit faults or antenna alignment problems.

Multimeter

A multimeter is one of the electronic technicians basic test instruments. It enables voltage, current and resistance to be accurately measured or checked. The battle still rages on between the exponents of analogue versus digital displays but, for this work, the increased ruggedness of a hand-held digital multimeter is by far the major consideration. The more expensive varieties come with a special impact-resistant holster which, it is alleged, will protect the enclosed instrument from damage when dropped from the top of a telegraph pole onto concrete. The viewing angle of a digital display is also less critical and consequently the instrument is potentially safer to use when working up ladders. The type with an audible continuity tester can be particularly useful when checking for open circuit cables.

Spectrum analyser

If expense is no object, a spectrum analyser is a good diagnostic tool. Depending on the polarization selected on the receiver, the entire range of co-polarized channels in a block may be displayed at the same time and any source of interference or unwanted attenuation can be detected. Faulty LNBs and polarizer faults can be quickly identified. The instrument is also ideal for programming optimal skew with frequency settings for each channel (where the facility exists). The basic operation of this instrument was described in Chapter 8.

Oscilloscope

An oscilloscope is useful for the diagnosis of video or audio signal path faults and the measurement of position sensor pulses from an actuator unit. A mains operated unit should be accompanied by the use of a portable isolation transformer. However, a number of good specification oscilloscopes are available with internal battery power and these are ideal for on-site servicing. As we will see waveform checks at certain key areas in the baseband path can quickly isolate a faulty stage. The standard oscilloscope used for general electronic servicing is a 20 MHz dual beam type.

Customer controls and indoor connections

The most common problem encountered will be tuning problems associated with the satellite receiver itself or ancillary tuning of the TV or VCR. If suspected perform the following checks:

1   Check that both the TV and VCR input stages are tuned to the RF output of the satellite receiver; check that the TV is tuned to the VCR RF modulator output.
2   Once (1) is checked then attention can be paid to the settings of the satellite tuner itself.
3   With models incorporating magnetic or mechanical polarizers with programmable skew setting, check that each channel is set to its optimum polarization.
4   With V/H switched types of polarizer check that the correct polarization sense is programmed for each required channel.
5   Check the connections at the rear of the equipment. Are all the cables present and connected correctly?

Visual check of the outdoor unit

A quick visual inspection of the outdoor unit is often a first step if you have good reason to suspect it. This would be when, say, sparklies were corrupting the picture quality or when FM noise only appears on the screen. In the case of multi-satellite motorized systems the actuator might be inoperative if only one satellite can be received. The main points to check are as follows:

1   Check that the antenna is pointing in the right general direction. In the absence of a neighbour's antenna as a guide, use a sighting compass.
2   Check for signs of vandalism. It is not uncommon for local 'drunks' or 'yobs' to alter antenna pointing or pull at cables 'for a laugh'. On occasions satellite antenna may be used for target shooting practice with air guns, catapults or even more exotic weapons. Another possibility is that a drawing pin or the like has been pushed into the cable thus creating a short.
3   Check cable condition and connections outdoors for corrosion, water ingress, poor contact or shorts. Check also whether the cable has been chafing on a corner stone, roof tile or guttering.

4   Check the tightness of the antenna mounting bolts. Does the antenna move in any direction with minimal effort?
5   Has the position of the head unit shifted in either focal length or rotation?
6   Has the ground been disturbed in the area of buried cables? If so a cable might be severed or damaged.
7   Check that the feedhorn cover or cap is not punctured, distorted or missing. If damaged or missing check that signs of insects or moisture are eradicated before refitting a new cap.
8   Check that water is not getting in between the connection of the feedhorn flange and the LNB. This often occurs if the bolts are not tight and the 'O' ring is not sufficiently compressed. If this is the case dry out with a hairdryer and reseal. This is a common cause of 'sparklies' with some systems.

Checking the subsystems

If all the above checks do not bear fruit then you have a genuine fault which must be tackled in a logical and systematic way. The first job is to isolate the subsystem which is causing the trouble. The following technique is as good as any and can usually be performed without removing the cover of the satellite receiver.

1   Check the output of the LNB with a signal strength meter; if a good reading is obtained then the LNB is probably satisfactory but it may still be low gain unless you have an absolute standard by which to assess it. This facility is normally only present on the more expensive signal strength meters. Another signal strength monitoring method is to measure the AGC line with a multimeter. On some models a convenient measuring point is brought out to the rear panel and this can also be used for antenna alignment. If in doubt about the gain of an LNB it is a fairly quick matter to substitute another without disturbing the antenna alignment.
2   If no output is obtained then check that the LNB supply voltage, typically in the range 12 to 24 V, is present both at the receiver LNB input socket and at the LNB end. When installing equipment this can easily be lost by carelessly shorting the coax outer braid to the central conductor while the equipment is switched on. If this voltage is missing then the likely fault is that an internal fuse has blown or a safety resistor has burned out. These resistors can easily be identified, since they are normally stood well off from the circuit board. Do not use standard resistors for replacement, use only the approved type recommended by the manufacturers or the equipment will not conform to the recognized safety standards. It is also important that the correct type of fuse is fitted; these can be either quick blow types identified by an F prefix to the value, or time-lag (anti-surge) prefixed by the letter T. Remember that the technician concerned will be held

legally responsible for any incidents occurring from careless servicing.

3   Check the polarization control circuitry. If signals are either missing or weak, or signals of only one polarization sense can be resolved, then it is possible that a fault in the polarization section is responsible. For V/H switched types, such as the Marconi unit fitted to many Astra packages, check that the voltage level shift of the LNB feed voltage, which switches the polarization, is 13 V for vertically polarized channels and 17 V for horizontally polarized channels. If these voltage level shifts occur and only one polarization sense can be received then suspect the head unit. With magnetic polarizers, which are current driven devices, insert a multimeter switched to the 200 mA range and check the current through the magnetic polarizer. Some designs select zero current for vertical polarization and between 40 mA and 80 mA for horizontal polarization. Others use a plus or minus current method to alter the polarization sense and often require − 40 mA or + 40 mA to select either vertical or horizontal polarization. Presence of the correct currents is normally sufficient to establish whether the subsystem is faulty. If a fault is detected then the most likely problem will be in the wiring. Finally, with the increasingly rare mechanical type of polarizer it is necessary to check that the 5 V supply is present, and check that control pulses are being sent to the servo motor. If the skew control still has little or no effect then suspect either that the probe has been bent or distorted or that the control circuitry is faulty. The chip normally used to provide the pulse output is derived from an inexpensive 555 timer chip.

4   Check the actuator circuit by observing that the antenna moves while the actuator is operated. If not check that the 36 V motor supply is reaching the actuator. Two people will be necessary for this task, one to measure the voltage at the actuator motor and the other to activate the positioner unit. Check that the position sensor is wired up correctly at both the indoor and outdoor connection points. Multi-satellite system cables are colour coded to aid this task. Incorrect wiring can burn out key components in the position sensor and this is often apparent by visual inspection. Persistent blowing of the actuator motor fuse indicates that either the motor power cable is short-circuited or more likely that the motor windings have shorted turns, or that the assembly is seized up. Also check that water is not getting into the actuator assembly and causing problems.

5   Check for continuity of cables. This can be performed by utilizing another length of cable. For example, to check the continuity between the ends of a long length of coax cable all that is needed is to bridge the inner conductor to the coax braid at one end with a short lead and two crocodile clips. Measuring the resistance between the central conductor and the braid at the other end will determine if either conductor is open circuit. A good cable should read nearly zero ohms. A similar method can be used for other long runs of cable by 'borrow-

ing' another length of cable used for another purpose. In this way, two lengths of cable can be checked at the same time. A shorted coaxial cable can be detected by checking the resistance between the central conductor and the outer braid (without the crocodile clip lead attached). If zero ohms is measured then a short circuit cable or connector is the fault.

Power supply faults

If the faulty section has still not been located by the above checks, or supply voltages/currents are found to be missing, the fault is most likely to be in the power supply of the receiver. In general, this area is the most unreliable section of most electronic equipment and with satellite receivers, this is no exception. This section of the receiver generates the supply voltages for its internal circuitry and also external feeds to the LNB, polarizer and actuator (where fitted). The first items to check are fuses and fusible safety resistors; these can go faulty at the drop of a hat and their failure does not necessarily indicate that a fault is present. Refitting a new one and switching on will determine if a fault is present. If it blows again then some other component is responsible for the fault. If it does not, the probability is that a transient pulse from the mains supply has caused it to blow. It is also not uncommon for fuses to fracture due to mechanical mishandling or faulty manufacture. In these cases a visual inspection of the fuse is often insufficient, since no detectable fracture is visible. The solution is to check each fuse, out of circuit, with a multimeter set to the ohms range. It should read about zero ohms. Figure 10.1 shows a representative power supply circuit. This particular one is fitted in the 'Tatung 1000 series' Astra satellite receivers.

Repairing a faulty power supply

If experience is gained in the area of diagnosis and repair of faulty power supplies then you will be equipped to deal with the majority of faults likely to occur in satellite equipment. The following is a guide to the repair of the power supply section.

Regulator chips

As can be seen from Figure 10.1 the power supply section of a typical satellite receiver consists of fixed voltage regulator chips, rated at 1 A, which are mounted on heatsinks or the outer casing. Receivers designed to control actuators will have an additional 36 V higher current supply. By measuring the input and output voltages a faulty chip is easily identified. If the input voltage is present and no output voltage is present the likelihood is that the chip is faulty. However, some of these chips have

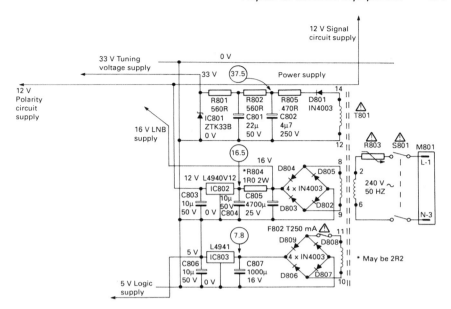

Figure 10.1 *Power supply used in the Tatung 1000 series Astra satellite receiver (Source: Tatung (UK) Ltd).*

short circuit protection so it could be possible for a short to be across the output. A resistance check from the output to chassis can be used to test for this. A 5 V regulator is often used to supply internal digital chips such as tuning processors and to supply the position sensor in motorized polar mounts. A 12 V regulator is often used to supply the video and audio processing circuitry and higher voltage regulators (15 V to 24 V) are used to supply LNB requirements. In the case of the circuit given in Figure 10.1 the LNB feed is unregulated and is taken direct from the reservoir capacitor C805. Where V/H switched types of polarizer are used, such as Astra receivers designed to work with the popular Marconi unit, a level-switched LNB supply is needed. In these cases a programmable regulator chip (1.2 V to 37 V programmable output) is employed which can be switched to produce either 13 V or 17 V LNB feed voltages. A possible fault, which is not uncommon with all regulator chips, is that they become temperature sensitive. That is to say they work satisfactorily for an hour or two and then shut down. If this is suspected a hairdryer can be used to accelerate the occurrence of the fault. When the fault appears, spraying the suspect chip with freezer often restores normal operation which indicates that the chip is faulty. By way of a guide, Figure 10.2 shows the pinout connections for a typical 1 A fixed regulator chip of the 78 series. Most other equivalent regulators have the same pinout connections.

Figure 10.2   *Pinout connections for 78 series or equivalent regulators*

Power supply diodes

Another fault that can occur, often with dramatic results in terms of fuse blowing, are short circuit bridge rectifier diodes such as D802 to D809 in Figure 10.1. This is primarily caused by transient pulses arriving from the mains supply possibly due to lightning. These can normally be checked with an analogue multimeter switched to the ohms range. The good diode should read approximately 1000 ohms in one direction and open circuit (i.e. infinite resistance) in the other direction. Some digital multimeters have a special diode check range, in which case a reading of 400 to 800 in one direction indicates a good diode.

Another type of diode which often crops up in power supplies is the zener diode which, when reverse biased, has a specific breakdown voltage. These diodes are usually labelled with their specific voltage and are used to stabilize a d.c. voltage very accurately. If the voltage across a zener diode exceeds its specific voltage value it can be deemed to be open circuit and in need of replacement. They can also become permanently short circuit although this is less likely to occur in practice.

Transformers

Mains transformers often give trouble; the most common fault is that the primary winding becomes open circuit. If this is suspected there will be no a.c. output voltage on the secondary windings. To confirm that it is the transformer at fault, ensure the mains is disconnected and measure the d.c. resistance across the primary winding with a multimeter switched to the ohms range. It should read just a few ohms if satisfactory. The secondary windings are rarely found to be faulty.

Power supply resistors and capacitors

Any component with a little triangle with an exclamation mark inside it (sometimes a diamond shape with a letter 'S' inside it) indicates that the component has been specially selected to conform with current safety regulations. Such marked components must be replaced by one of an identical type supplied by the manufacturers. Experience has shown that these become weak links in power supply circuits and can fail at the drop of a hat. When confronted with a power supply fault, experience has shown that a safety resistor being open circuit is the most likely culprit. Personally, I like safety regulations because it provides 'built in unreliability' which of course is the service technician's bread and butter (or should I say wholemeal and polyunsaturated spread). Any resistor connected in series with a supply line is prone to failure and should be checked. Some receivers, such as the Tatung 1000 series, have a safety thermistor (temperature sensitive resistor) with a positive temperature coefficient (PTC). This component, R803 in Figure 10.1, is located on the primary side of the mains transformer. The purpose of this resistor is to provide a low resistance at normal working temperatures, but when a fault is present the increased current flow causes the PTC to heat up, resulting in a rapid increase in resistance which limits the current to a safe value. These components often replace the conventional mains input fuse but they can go open circuit permanently. It is important that they be replaced with an identical type.

Electrolytic capacitors have a tendency to become open circuit particularly if old or exposed to heat and high voltages. A quick practical method of checking them is to 'rock them'. If they are dried out the chances are that one of the connection pins rots and can easily be detached exposing evidence of 'capacitor excreta' underneath. Distortion or shrinkage of the outer plastic sheath is also a tell-tale sign of a faulty electrolytic capacitor. If either of these methods fail then they can be removed and checked on a capacitance meter if suspected. An open circuit reservoir or smoothing capacitor is often detected by a significant reduction in the expected d.c. voltage across it.

Switched-mode power supplies

Power supplies incorporating regulators, although simple to diagnose and repair tend to run very warm. To reduce this problem and improve efficiency an alternative method of deriving the required voltages is sometimes used, called a switched-mode power supply. Most modern TV sets derive their power supplies by a similar method and most TV technicians will be familiar with them. Quite high voltages (mains potential) are present on the primary side of the circuit and consequently servicing should be left to suitably qualified personnel. Dabbling could lead to major damage or possible electrocution. A common switched-mode power supply circuit is based around the Siemens TDA 4600 series control IC and is often found in satellite receivers of European origin. The essential features of this type of power supply, fitted in the Grundig STR20 series of satellite receivers, is shown greatly simplified in Figure 10.3.

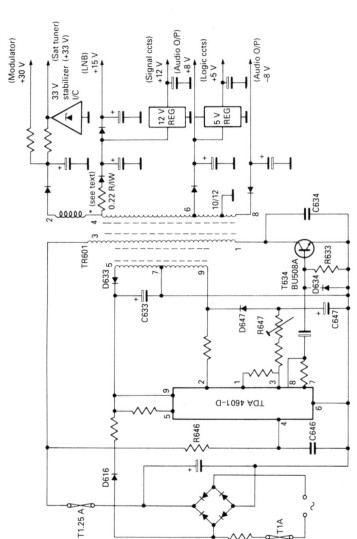

Figure 10.3 TDA 4600 switched mode power supply (simplified)

Basic circuit operation

When the chopper transistor T634 is switched on, current flows in the primary of TR601 thus energy is temporarily stored in the transformer. The secondary windings can only draw current related to this stored energy. When the chopper transistor is switched off the magnetic field collapses and current flows through the rectifiers in the secondary circuits (to the right of the transformer) thus charging the associated reservoir capacitors. The time the chopper is switched on determines the maximum secondary current. Feedback pulses are derived from pin 9 of the transformer and these are fed to the control IC at pin 2. The result is that internal logic within the chip causes the chopper transistor to be switched on when the magnetic field has fully collapsed. Regulation is provided by controlling the time at which the chopper transistor is to switch off. A feedback voltage, proportional to the current drawn, is derived from the winding connected between pins 7 and 9 of the transformer, rectified by D647 and fed to pin 3 of the IC. Internal control circuitry within the chip controls the time that the chopper is to switch off. The basic switching frequency is controlled by R646 and C646 which are supplied from a mains rectified 300 V line. This provides stabilization against variation of mains input voltages. Internal circuitry within the control IC discharges C646 during the chopper transistor's off time. The output voltages are set by the adjustment of R647 which controls the feedback to pin 3 of the IC, and should be set up whilst monitoring the +15 V line.

Overcurrent protection is incorporated in the control IC by counting the variable mark to space pulses. An increase in the designed working current, due to a possible fault condition, results in the frequency of oscillation falling. When this falls to beyond a certain preset value then internal fixed switching within the chip takes over and thus limits the current.

Overvoltage protection is provided by an increase in the frequency of operation and would happen in cases where, say, a secondary supply line is open circuit and less current is being drawn.

An initial start up supply is provided by D616 and this should be at least 7 V. Once oscillation has started the chip supply is fed from a transformer-derived voltage of about 12 V via D633/C633. If the mains input is too low, protection is provided by the start up voltage being below the 7 V threshold thus causing the power supply not to start up. Similarly, the voltage present at pin 5 of the IC should be greater than 2.2 V or the chip shuts down.

Typical faults

If R646 goes high in value or C646 is open circuit the chopper transistor will blow (become short circuit). If failure of the chopper transistor is experienced always change R646, even if it appears to read correctly on an ohmeter. Failure to do this will almost certainly lead to a recall at some later date with another blown chopper. It is very rare these days for choppers to blow unless some underlying fault is also present. In general, failure of high value resistors in power supplies is often the cause of repeated failure of the chopper transistor.

If the adjustment of R647 has no effect on the output voltage then the chances are that C647 is open circuit or dried out. If the power supply fails to start on occasions, check C633 by substitution. If the power supply will not start up at all, check that the rectifiers in the secondary circuit are not short circuit and that at least 7 V is present at pin 9 of the IC at switch on. If this value is well over 12 V then the chip is faulty. Other diagnostic checks that can be made are the presence of a 4 V square wave at pin 1 of the IC and square wave drive of at least 1 V amplitude at pin 7. Likewise this waveform should be present at the base of the chopper transistor. If T634 is ever found to be faulty always check the components D634, R633 and C632 and replace R646 before fitting a replacement transistor.

All the supplies fed from the secondary winding of the transformer usually incorporate low value safety resistors, fitted before the rectifiers, these can go open circuit. The one fitted in the LNB supply line usually blows if a prolonged short is present on the coaxial cable during installation. This particular component is marked with an asterisk on Figure 10.3.

Dry joints can be a problem in these power supplies, particularly on the pin out connections of wound components. This is because they tend to vibrate at the working frequency which often results in solder joints cracking in a circular pattern round the pins.

Faults in the head unit and tuner/demodulator

If the LNB is found to be faulty, repair should not be attempted and it should be sent back to the manufacturer or supplier for an exchange unit. The compact layout of components using surface mounted technology necessitates specialist repair. Likewise, the polarizer/feedhorn assembly is not serviceable since, with magnetic polarizers in particular, the windings are embedded into the feedhorn itself. Each component part of the head unit can thus be considered as a module for replacement only.

The tuner/demodulator can, as its name implies, contain the 1st IF tuner unit (950 MHz to 1750 MHz) and the Fm demodulator. Again, the layout is critical and a lot of surface mounted technology is employed necessitating complete replacement as a unit rather than repair. In any case, the time spent diagnosing and replacing an internal faulty component will probably cost more than the replacement of the entire unit. The module's many pins will need to be unsoldered and the unit removed from the receiver for replacement. This should not be attempted unless a special desoldering tool is to hand, or damage to the printed circuit will result. A 'one shot' suction type desoldering tool with a plastic nozzle can be acquired quite cheaply to remove the molten solder from each connection. However, the plastic nozzles are short lived and experience has shown that a better type to use is one with a built in soldering iron which allows single handed removal of solder from the many connections. The nozzle, made of metal, is also the bit of the soldering iron and subsequently has a long working life.

Magnetic polarizer control

The purpose of a magnetic polarizer control circuit is to maintain a constant current through the polarizer windings over a wide range of outdoor temperature conditions. With low cost receivers designed to receive single satellite transmissions this is often all that is provided. However higher priced receivers and multi-satellite equipments provide for additional fine trimming of the polarizer current whose value can be indirectly stored to take into account skew with frequency effects. The reason for this is that the degree of wave-twisting is not constant and varies with frequency. With simple receivers the physical polarizer orientation must be set at a compromise position for best cross polar rejection over the required frequency band.

One method for achieving a constant current through the polarizer is shown in Figure 10.4 and is used in the Tatung 1000 series of Astra receivers.

The polarizer is required to select either vertically or horizontally polarized signals. The direction of current flowing through the magnetic polarizer, and thus polarization selection, is controlled by the output from pin

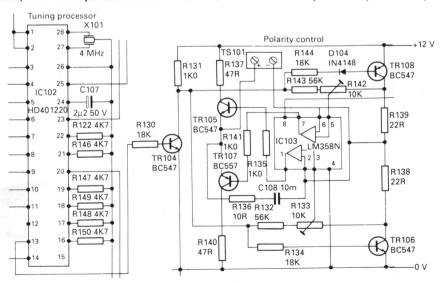

Figure 10.4 *Polarity control circuit (Source: Tatung (UK) Ltd)*

13 of the microprocessor IC102: a logic 'high' for vertical and 'low' for horizontal. This output is used to switch TR104 which in turn controls TR106 and TR108. These two transistors are used to switch the current direction and select the polarity of the received signals.

For horizontally polarized signals TR105 and TR106 are switched on and TR107 and TR108 are switched off. Current flows out through TR105's emitter, through the polarizer winding and back to 0 V via TR106. The required current value, preset by R133, is compared with that measured through R138 and any correction to the current is controlled via IC 103 output on pin 1, by TR105.

For vertically polarized signals TR107 and TR108 are switched on and TR105 and TR106 are switched off, thus current flows in the opposite direction out through the polarizer via TR108 and TR107. The corresponding current level is set by R142. The required current value, preset by R142, is compared with that measured through R139 and any correction to the current is controlled via IC103 output on pin 7, by TR107.

The most likely faults to be encountered in this type of circuit are failure of the switching transistor/s or faulty presets R142 and R143.

Baseband, video and audio processing circuits

For fault-finding in this area an oscilloscope is useful. By the strategic monitoring of waveforms at signal inputs and outputs of the various stages the fault can usually be quickly isolated to a particular stage and the appropriate action taken. Alternatively, a low cost signal injector can be used to inject a signal loaded with high frequency harmonics at the input/outputs of various stages. The resulting video patterning on the screen or audio breakthrough (or lack of it) can often be used to deduce the faulty stage. Components most likely to fail are electrolytic capacitors and semiconductors.

Digital and remote control circuitry

Digital circuits, such as microprocessors and remote control circuitry are very reliable in practice and are rarely found to be faulty. In cases where a fault is suspected in this area, the first thing to do is to check that the various supply voltages to the chips are present. Secondly, check the clock frequencies with an oscilloscope or frequency counter since crystals, used to keep the frequency of oscillation stable and accurate, can either be off frequency or drift with temperature, replacement being the only cure. It is very rare for microprocessors to go faulty, so suspect these chips last.

Remote control circuitry can sometimes give trouble, but 99 times out of a 100 it is the handset which is faulty, not the receiving circuitry. An infra-red remote control tester is a valuable addition to the toolbox, so that each function button of a suspected handset can be quickly checked for both operation and range. The most common cause of handset failure is tea, coffee, or other liquid being spilled, in which case it is necessary to dismantle and clean up with methylated spirit and a brush. However, with the membrane type of keypad replacement is normally necessary.

Twiddling

When confronted with a faulty receiver it is tempting to start the whole-sale twiddling of presets and other adjustable components. This should be avoided like the plague, unless you have good reason to suspect maladjustment. If for any reason you do, always mark its original adjust-ment position so that it may be reset precisely to its original position afterwards. Out of control twiddling can render a whole receiver useless or require extensive manufacturer's set up procedures to be followed which may be both tedious and need expensive equipment. A golden rule: never twiddle unless you know precisely what the adjustment is for.

A workshop servicing aid

Faults other than power supply faults are likely to be destined for work-shop service. For signal path faults a compatible antenna/head unit will be needed to test or effect repairs to the receiver. For example, dedicated Astra receivers have been sold in relatively large numbers but one of the main problems when encountering a faulty satellite receiver destined for workshop service is the interface to its dish/LNB assembly. The chances are that the receiver/dish combination installed at the workshop is in-compatible with the receiver on the service bench. Complications arise with the polarization requirements. Some systems use single coax and others need one or more extra polarizer wires. The lack of standardiz-ation between different manufacturers' designs is often a headache to technicians in the front line. The concept of perhaps eight different outdoor units, corresponding to as many manufacturers, adorning the workshop wall is obviously not practical. There are elaborate test gener-ators available that can be used to simulate a satellite broadcast but these tend to be expensive and out of the range of the average technician at the present time.

So what can be done to overcome this problem at a lower cost? The solution is to fit an antenna with the most commonly encountered head unit at the workshop site and control the polarizer manually, from a separate unit, for connection to less common receivers. The following section describes a low cost servicing aid designed to feed the head unit of the V/H switched Marconi LNB. This head unit is fitted to the vast majority of Astra systems currently installed in the UK. The servicing aid, in conjunction with an antenna incorporating the Marconi head unit, provides a two-way, d.c. isolated 960 MHz to 1700 MHz signal to feed any other make of Astra satellite receiver.

The Marconi LNB

The majority of readily available Astra equipment uses an offset focus 65 cm dish and a low cost Marconi LNB which together achieve good results, even in heavy rain. However, an 85 cm dish is necessary north of latitude 55°N. The LNB, feedhorn and polarizer requirements are all fitted into a single strong casting. The manufacturers using this LNB, at the time of writing, include Amstrad, Sakura, Ferguson and Alba. The Marconi LNB uses a remotely switched pair of probes spaced at 90° and either can be switched in for reception of vertical or horizontal polarized signals. All the necessary polarization and LNB supply voltages are sent up a single screened coax cable. This convenience is achieved by utilizing a voltage level shift method of switching the polarizer with approximately 13 V for vertical polarization and 17 V for horizontal polarization. These d.c. voltages are sent up the cable to the LNB from a matched receiver. The 960 MHz to 1700 MHz down-converted signal from the LNB is fed down to the receiver.

LNB interface unit

The interface unit is designed with the assumption that a Marconi head unit is used with the antenna. The unit provides all the necessary voltages to feed the LNB and provides for manual switching between vertical and horizontal polarization. A single output of 960 MHz to 1700 MHz is

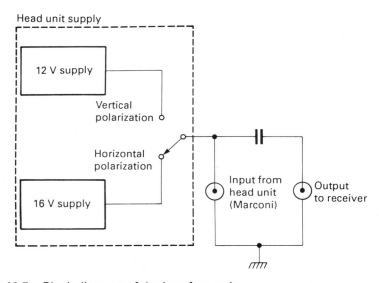

Figure 10.5 *Block diagram of the interface unit*

provided for connection to any make of receiver. No d.c. voltages from the interface unit are applied to the receiver under test and likewise no d.c. voltages from the receiver are allowed to the unit or LNB. The output of the interface is thus analogous to a simple aerial for Astra satellite receivers.

To feed a Marconi LNB we need a 13.5 V d.c. source and a 16.5 V d.c. source as previously described. Since the Marconi device is threshold operated at slightly below +15 V a +12 V supply can be used for vertical polarization and a +16 V supply for horizontal polarization. A block diagram of the interface is shown in Figure 10.5. Either + 12 V or + 16 V is sent to supply the LNB depending on the setting of the single pole two-way LNB supply switch. This corresponds to the two polarization switching voltages for the LNB.

Design details

The unit was designed around the 78 series of voltage regulator ICs. These all have internal overload, thermal, and short circuit protection. The latter is particularly important since it is common to find shorts in F connector plug wiring. The 7812 gives an output of 12 V (+ / − 0.5 V) from an input range 14.5 to 30 V and the 7815 gives 15 V (+ / − 0.6 V) from an input range of 17.5 to 30 V. Both chips contain eighteen transistors, two zener diodes and twenty resistors. Higher voltages can be gained from 78 serious chips, with slightly reduced regulation as a penalty, by the inclusion of a simple programming resistor. A variant of this technique is used for the + 16 V supply derived from a 7815 chip.

The input voltage $+ V_{in}$ must be at least + 2.5 V greater than $+ V_o$. The output voltage V_o, is equal to $V_r + IR$ where V_r equals the basic regulator voltage (see Figure 10.6).

The typical value for I is 1.5 mA. Therefore to obtain 16 V output from a 15 V chip:

$$R = V_o - V_r / I = 16 - 15/0.0015 = 1 \text{ k ohm approx.}$$

In view of the inconsistent values of I for different chips R should be made variable. An alternative approach to obtain a small increase in the fixed

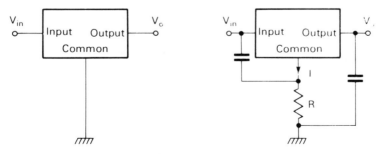

Figure 10.6 *Basic 78 series circuits*

regulator voltage, without the corresponding reduction in regulation, is to utilize the fixed voltage drop of silicon diodes instead of a programming resistor. This is the technique that will be used to derive the 16 V supply from a 7815, 15 V fixed regulator in the final circuit.

Because of the wide input voltage range the choice of mains transformer is wide. For example, the output of a 15 V secondary when rectified and applied across a large value reservoir capacitor will provide a d.c. voltage of:

$$V_{in} = 15 \text{ V} \times 1.414 = 21.2 \text{ V}$$

Therefore any transformer with a secondary winding in the range 15 V to 20 V can be used. I reclaimed a transformer from a scrap Sanyo Betamax video recorder. However if one is not to hand a 50 VA 15 V transformer can be obtained from RS Components/Electromail or any number of other component suppliers.

The circuit

The complete circuit diagram is shown in Figure 10.7. Inputs and outputs to the chips are RF bypassed with 0.1 µF disc ceramic capacitors to prevent oscillation and reduce noise. These should be mounted as close as possible to the actual chip input and output pins. D5 to D8 provide

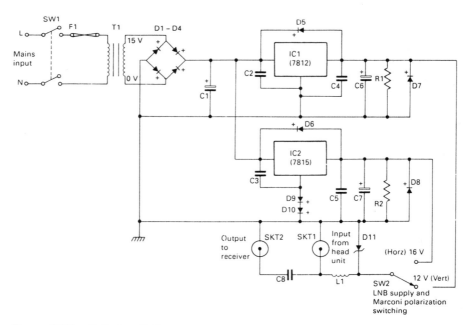

Figure 10.7 *Full circuit diagram*

extra protection for the chips under prolonged reverse voltage conditions. R1 and R2 provide a constant load for the regulator chips. The two diodes, D9 and D10 provide an extra 1.2 V increase to the 15 V output of IC2 thus lifting the output voltage to about 16.2 V.

The series d.c. blocking capacitor C8 forms a high pass filter with the shunt 75 ohm impedance of the cable, R. The frequency to be passed is approximately 1 GHz. At 3 dB down the reactance $(X_c) = R$ so the series capacitor can be calculated as follows:

$$R = X_c$$
$$\text{so } R = 1/(2\pi fC)$$
$$\text{so } C = 1/(2\pi fR)$$
$$= 1/(6.28)\,(10^9)\,(7.5)\,(10)$$
$$= (2.1)\,(10^{-12})\text{ F}$$
$$= 2.2\text{ pF}$$

The suggested value is made ten times larger to allow for tolerances and approximations; a value of 22 pf is reasonable. For a 'belt and braces' approach two 47 pf capacitors could be used in series to cover the unlikely event that a single capacitor might go short circuit causing possible damage to the receiver. An RF choke, L1, is inserted to isolate the d.c. supply from the RF signal. A few turns of enamelled copper wire on a ferrite bead is sufficient. A suitable choke can be reclaimed from an old scrap TV. An 18 V zener diode, D11, is added for overvoltage protection. This will conduct heavily or go short circuit if the supply voltage exceeds 18 V under possible fault conditions, thus protecting the LNB from damage.

Construction

The circuit can be constructed on a scrap of matrix board measuring about 5 cm by 10 cm, using the components listed in Table 10.1. The transformer and circuit board are then housed in a plastic instrument case. A suitable case measuring 130 mm × 125 mm × 68 mm can be purchased from a local Tandy store. This case is ideal since it has a thick plastic front panel for ease of drilling and filing, and a metal rear panel which can be used as a heatsink for the regulator chips. An ovoid hole is precut in the rear panel to facilitate a strain relief bushing for the two core mains cable. A full parts list, Table 10.1, is provided for convenience. Extra care must be taken to make leads to and from the high frequency areas very short (less than 3 cm). All the sockets and switches, with the exception of the mains switch, are best grouped together as close as possible to keep wiring short. The d.c. blocking capacitor, C8, is best wired directly between the centre pins of the adjacently mounted SKT1 and SKT2. The RF choke, L1, should also be mounted as close to SKT2 as possible. At high frequencies, stray reactive qualities of internal wiring can have a significant effect on the signal to noise ratio and introduce

Table 10.1   *Components list*

Capacitors:	
C1	4700 μF, 63 V electrolytic
C2-C5	0.1 μF, disc ceramic
C6-C7	22 μF, 25 V electrolytic
C8	22 pF, disc ceramic.
Resistors:	
R1-R2	470 R, 0.5W
Semiconductors:	
IC1	7812 or equivalent
IC2	7815 or equivalent
D1-D4	1 A bridge rectifier (eg BY164, RS261-328 or 4 × BY127)
D5-D10	IN4 001 or similar
D11	BZX79C18 or similar 18 V zener diode.
Miscellaneous:	
F1	T315 mA
L1	A few turns of enamelled copper wire on ferrite bead
T1	50 VA mains transformer with 15–24 V secondary
SKT1-SKT2	Panel mounted UHF coaxial sockets or F connector sockets
SW1	DPDT subminiature switch (250 V rated)
SW2	SPDT subminiature switch.

Instrument case, e.g. Tandy 130 mm × 125 mm × 68 mm
Plastic strain relief bush
Insulated mounting kit for 7 815 chip
Mains plug and three metres of mains cable
Mounting bolts, nuts and washers for coax sockets
20 mm panel mounted fuseholder
5 cm × 10 cm (approx.) piece of matrix board (e.g. Veroboard).

instability. The LNB input socket and the signal output socket are standard panel mounted UHF coax sockets. For maximum flexibility, an extra pair of F connector in-line conversion plugs may be useful. This will alleviate the need for extra F connector sockets and associated wiring.

Another point worth mentioning is that the common terminal (centre pin) on 78 series chips is connected to the heatsink surface. If the 16 V LNB supply chip (7815) is not insulated from the chassis, RV1 will be effectively short circuited and the output will be the basic regulator voltage, + 15 V. This will lead to intermittent and unpredictable voltage level switching of the polarizer. [This had me stumped for a few minutes during the testing stage!]. After assembly and before connection to the LNB and test receiver, measure the various outputs and check that they are correct with both settings of the switch. Any mistakes here could ruin the LNB and/or receiver. Check also that no d.c. is present on SKT2 (the one to which the receiver is connected).

Using the unit

After voltage testing connect the LNB input to SKT1 and the receiver to SKT2 and switch on the unit and receiver. Most makes of receiver usually signal whether vertical or horizontal polarization is appropriate for any selected channel. The polarization switch, SW2, on the interface unit is thus manually switched, as appropriate, to comply with the polarization indicated. The unit has proved useful in the workshop both for servicing and testing Astra satellite receivers prior to installation, and many different makes of receiver have been successfully operated via the unit. There is no noticeable deterioration in the signal level or quality with the unit connected and it can be left switched on for any length of time (to deal with intermittent faults) without overheating. It is also a wise precaution to check the actual receiver d.c. voltages destined for the LNB supply since this is a possible fault condition. A resistor lead can be pushed into the central section of the receiver's F connector socket to provide a measuring point. It is not advisable to have measuring points on the unit's front panel since the extra wiring can lead to stability problems.

Appendix 1

Glossary of terms

Absolute zero: The temperature at which all molecular movement ceases; zero degrees kelvin (0°K) or −273 degrees Celsius (−273°C).

ADC: Analogue to digital conversion.

AFC: Automatic frequency control used to lock onto, and maintain, frequency of the selected signal.

Alignment: Fine tuning to maximize sensitivity in a selected channel.

AM: Amplitude modulation.

Amplifier: A circuit that increases the power or voltage of a signal.

Apogee: The highest point (maximum altitude) of a geocentric orbit.

Aperture: The microwave collection area of a dish.

Aspect ratio: The ratio of screen width to height. HDTV is 16:9 and conventional TV is 4:3.

Attenuation: A signal level loss.

Attenuator: A circuit that decreases the power of a signal.

AZ: Azimuth.

Azimuth: The angle between an antenna beam and the meridian plane (horizontal plane).

Bandpass filter: A circuit which passes a restricted band of frequencies. Unwanted lower and upper frequencies are attenuated.

Bandwidth: The total range of frequencies occupied by a signal; window of receiver, etc.

Baseband: The band of frequencies containing the information before modulation; general term for audio and video signals in AV links.

Baud: The accepted unit of digital data-transmission rate.

BBS: Business band service.

Beamwidth: The antenna acceptance angle measured between half power points (3 dB down points).

BER: Bit error rate – a measure of digital demodulation or decoding accuracy.

Bird: A quaint Americanism for satellite.

Bit: A binary digit (a '1' or an '0').

Bit rate: The number of digital bits transmitted per second.

Boresight: Central axis of symmetry in a paraboloid dish – the beam centre.

Carrier: The radio frequency wave upon which the baseband signal is modulated.

Cassegrain: A dish using a convex subreflector and a paraboloid main reflector.

CATV: Community (cable) antenna television.

C-band: Satellite frequencies in the 4/6 GHz band.

CCI: Co-channel interference.

CCIR: International Radio Consultative Committee.

Chrominance: The colour information in a composite video signal.

C/I: Ratio of carrier signal to interference.

Clamp: Video processing circuit designed to remove unwanted low frequencies.

Clark orbit: A geosynchronous equatorial orbit in which a satellite appears stationary north-to-south with respect to an observer at the earth's surface.

CNR or C/N: Carrier to noise ratio.

Composite baseband: The raw demodulator output before filtering, clamping and decoding.

Composite video: A complete video signal, including luminance, sync and colour information but not audio or data subcarriers.

CP: Circular polarization.

Cross polarized: Of the opposite polarization.

Crosstalk: Interference between cross polarized or adjacent channels.

DAC: Digital to analogue conversion.

dB: Decibels; a logarithmic ratio normally used to express the difference between two powers (dBs = 10 log P2/P1).

dBi: The gain of an antenna relative to an isotropic source.

dBm: dB power relative to a 1 milliwatt standard.

dBw: dB power relative to one watt.

DBS: Direct broadcasting by satellite or direct broadcasting service.

Declination: The angle between the equatorial plane and antenna beam.

De-emphasis: The reversal of pre-emphasis by reducing the amplitude of high frequency components and noise.

Demodulation: The recovery of baseband information from a modulated carrier.

Deviation: The maximum amount the carrier frequency is shifted by the modulating message or baseband signal.

Discrimination: The ability of a circuit to separate wanted from unwanted signals.

Discriminator: One type of circuit used to demodulate an FM signal.

Down-conversion: Reducing a band of high frequencies to a lower band.

DSO: Dielectric stabilized oscillator used in LNB design.

DTH: Direct to home.

EBU: European Broadcasting Union.

Eclipse protected: A satellite which continues transmission in spite of a solar eclipse.

ECS: European communications satellite.

EDTV: Extra definition television.

EIRP: Equivalent isotropically radiated power, combining the transmitter (or transponder) rf power and the transmitting antenna gain.

EL: Elevation.

Elevation: The angle between the antenna beam and the horizontal. Measured in the vertical plane.

EL/AZ: An antenna with independent steering both in azimuth and elevation.

Energy dispersal: A low frequency signal added to the baseband signal before modulation. Used to reduce the peak power per unit bandwidth of an FM signal in order to reduce its interference potential.

EOL: End of life of a satellite.

ERP: Effective radiated power.

ESA: European Space Agency.

Eutelsat: European Telecommunications Satellite Organization.

F/D: The ratio of focal length to diameter of a dish.

Feedhorn: A small wide-beam antenna system (usually horn shaped) that collects the energy reflected from the dish.

FET: Field effect transistor. A type of low noise transistor relying on electric fields, rather than simple pn junctions.

FM: A transmission system in which the modulating waveform is made to vary the carrier frequency.

Footprint: The area on the earth's surface, for a given dish size, within which a signal from a satellite is judged to be of acceptable quality.

Free space loss: The attenuation between transmitter and receiver.

FSS: Fixed satellite service.

Gain: The ratio of output power to input power, normally expressed in dB form.

GaAsFET: Gallium arsenide field effect transistor (used in LNBs).

GEO: Geosynchronous equatorial orbit. (See Clark orbit.)

Geosychronous: An orbit having a period equal to that of the earth's rotation but not necessarily geostationary.

Ground noise: Spurious microwave signals generated from ground temperature.

G/T: Gain to noise-temperature ratio (a figure of merit of a satellite receiving system).

Giga (G): One billion.

GHz: A frequency of 1 000 million cycles per second (1 000 MHz).

Global beam: Satellite footprint which covers the entire visible earth's surface.

Frequency: Number of cycles per second measured in Hz.

Half-transponder: A compromise method of sending two TV signals through one transponder.

HEMT: High electron mobility transistor (low noise device used in LNBs).

HDTV: High definition television.

Head unit: Combination of LNB, polarizer and feedhorn.

High pass filter: A circuit which only passes signals above a designed frequency.

High-power satellite: A loose expression, normally taken to mean greater than 100 watts transponder power.

Hz: Hertz (1 cycle per second).

IF: Intermediate frequency.

IMD: Intermodulation distortion.

ITU: International Telecommunications Union.

Isolator: A device with high signal loss in one direction but low in the other.

Isotropic: Ideally, a point source which transmits signals of equal power in all directions.

Kelvin scale: An absolute temperature scale in which the zero of the scale is −273 degrees Celsius (−273°C).

Ku-band: Frequencies within the range 10.7 to 18 GHz.

Linked budget: Overall calculation of power gains and losses from transmission to reception.

Link margin: Amount in dBs by which *C/N* ratio exceeds the receiver's demodulator threshold *C/N* value.

LHCP: Left hand circular polarization.

LNA: Low noise amplifier.

LNB: Low noise block (down-converter). One type of LNC which down-converts a block of frequencies in one go.

LNC: Low noise converter (term often includes the LNB).

Low pass filter: A circuit which only passes signals lower than a designed frequency.

Low power satellite: Transponder power less than 30 watts.

LPF: Low pass filter.

Luminance: Light and shade information in a TV signal (contrast).

MAC: Multiplexed analogue components colour system.

Magnetic variation: Difference between true north and that indicated by a compass (also called magnetic declination).

MATV: Master antenna television system.

Medium power satellite: Loose term for power between 30 and 100 watts.

Modulation index: The ratio of peak deviation to the highest modulating frequency.

Mount: The structure which supports the antenna.

Multiplexing: A single transmission channel carrying two or more independent signals.

Noise figure (NF): Ratio of the noise contributed by a practical amplifier to an ideal noise-free amplifier measured at some reference temperature. Usually expressed in dB.

Noise temperature (NT): Noise measurement of an amplifying system expressed as the absolute temperature of a resistance delivering the same noise power.

NTSC: National Television Standards Commission (USA).

Offset-fed antenna: An antenna with a reflector that forms only part of a true paraboloid in order to minimize blockage caused by the feed and its support structure.

OMT: Orthogonal mode transducer, a waveguide device which separates (or combines) two orthogonally polarized signals.

Orthogonal: At right angles to each other.

Outdoor unit: See Head Unit.

PAL: Phase alternate line colour system employing a delay line.

Paraboloid: Classical shape of the antenna reflector.

Path distance: See Slant Range.

Perigree: Lowest point or minimum altitude in a geocentric orbit.

Period (1): Time taken for a satellite to complete one orbital revolution.

Period (2): The time taken for one cycle of a sinusoidal waveform.

PFD: Power flux density (related to field strength).

Phase distortion: Due to a non-linear relationship between amplifier phase shift and frequency.

PLL: Type of demodulator relying on a phase locked loop.

Polar mount: Antenna mechanism allowing tracking of the geo-arc.

Polarization: The plane or direction of one of the fields (usually the E field) in an electromagnetic wave.

pp: peak to peak.

Pre-emphasis: The procedure for improving the signal to noise ratio of a transmission by emphasizing the higher baseband frequencies.

Prime focus: The focus of a paraboloid dish.

Rain outage: Loss of Ku-band signal caused by heavy rain absorption.

Reference signal: Highly stable signal used to compare other signals.

RF: Radio frequency.

RGB: The three primary colours, red green and blue.

RHCP: Right hand circular polarization.

RRO: Radio receive only.

Saturation: The colour intensity parameter in a video signal.

SAW: Surface acoustic wave filter. A device designed to shape the frequency response of a signal. Can replace many tuned circuits.

S-band: 2.6 GHz band.

Scaler feed: Wide corrugated horn feed.

SECAM: Sequence colour à Mémoire (a French TV standard).

Semi-DBS: Popular term for medium power satellite providing DTH programming.

Sidelobe: Response of a dish to signals off the central axis.

Skew: The twist difference in polarization angle between satellites.

Slant range: Total path length between satellite and a receiver on earth.

SMATV: Satellite master antenna television.

SNR or S/N: Signal to noise ratio.

Solar outage: Signal loss due to sun's position, relative to receiving station.

Sparklies: Popular term for impulse noise spikes visible as annoying black or white flashes over the screen.

Spillover: Usable signal, normally outside expected range.

Spot beam: Circular or elliptical beam covering some defined region of the earth's surface.

Stag's head: Term used to describe a wall mounted antenna.

Subcarrier: An information carrying wave which modulates the main carrier.

Sync: Synchronization.

TDM: Tuner/demodulator in the indoor unit or receiver.

Thermal noise: Random electric variations caused by molecular motion which increases with temperature.

TEM: Transverse electromagnetic wave.

Threshold: Term used in an FM signal where the normally linear relationship between C/N and demodulated signal S/N no longer holds.

Threshold extension: A technique for lowering the C/N value at which non-linear demodulator effects start.

Transponder: Powered equipment on a satellite used to re-broadcast the uplink signal down to earth-located receivers (the downlink).

Trap: Jargon for any device which attenuates a selective frequency band.

Truncation: Loss of the outer side-frequencies of an FM signal due to filters, displayed on the screen as 'tearing' on video transients.

TVRO: Television receive only.

TWT: Travelling wave tube.

UHF: 300 MHz to 3 GHz band.

VCO: Voltage controlled oscillator sometimes called VTO (voltage tuned oscillator).

VSWR: Voltage standing wave ratio; a measurement of impedance mismatch conditions on an antenna, waveguide or transmission line system.

WARC: World Administrative Radio Conference. The International Telecommunications Union meetings for determining radio communication standards.

Weighting: Correction of S/N measurements after allowing for subjective annoyance factors.

Appendix 2

Suppliers of satellite equipment and spares (mostly trade only)

Combined Precision Components PLC (CPC). 186–200 North Road, Preston, Lancashire PR1 1YP (Supply of Volex Radex cables; 'Twist-on' connectors; Kathrein signal strength meters and other sundries at competitive prices). Tel. (0772) 555034.

HRS Ltd. Garrets Green Lane, Birmingham B33 0UE. (Supply of complete satellite systems; cables; accessories; spares and low cost signal strength meters of the 'in line' type). Tel. (021) 789 7575.

Merseyside Satellite Consultants. Antenna House, Atherton Road, Aintree, Liverpool L9 7EL. (Supply of a wide range of satellite systems; cables; LNBs; antennae; polarizers; OMTs; actuators and all hardware items including T & K brackets). Tel. (051) 523 5000.

Micro-X. Unit 2 Drury Way Industrial Estate, Laxcon Close, London NW10 0TG. (Supply of complete systems; cables; MASPRO signal strength meters and all installation accessories). Tel. 01 459 1200.

Multi Aerial Distributors. The Aerial Centre, Horsham Road, Ellens Green, West Sussex, RH12 3AS (C.O.D. plus carriage supply of Volex Radex cables; F connectors; Sat seal roof tiles; stands; brackets and masts; also complete systems). Tel. (0403) 723423/723427.

Network Satellite Systems. Units 7, 8 & 9, Newburn Bridge Industrial Estate, Hartlepool, Cleveland, England TS25 1UB (Supply of a wide range of satellite equipment; test equipment and accessories): Tel. 0429 86966.

Webro (Long Eaton) Ltd. Mayfair Building, Oxford Street, Long Eaton, Nottingham NG10 1JR. (Supply of Pope cables). Tel. (0602) 724483/724209/730114.

Appendix 3

Footprint maps of UK popular satellites

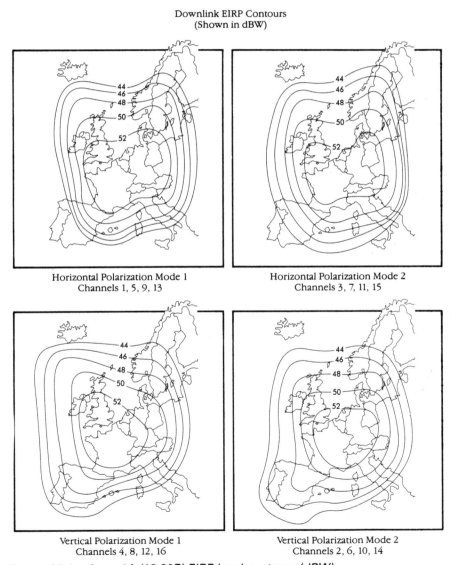

Downlink EIRP Contours
(Shown in dBW)

Horizontal Polarization Mode 1
Channels 1, 5, 9, 13

Horizontal Polarization Mode 2
Channels 3, 7, 11, 15

Vertical Polarization Mode 1
Channels 4, 8, 12, 16

Vertical Polarization Mode 2
Channels 2, 6, 10, 14

Figure A3.1 *Astra 1A (19.2 °E) EIRP level contours (dBW)*

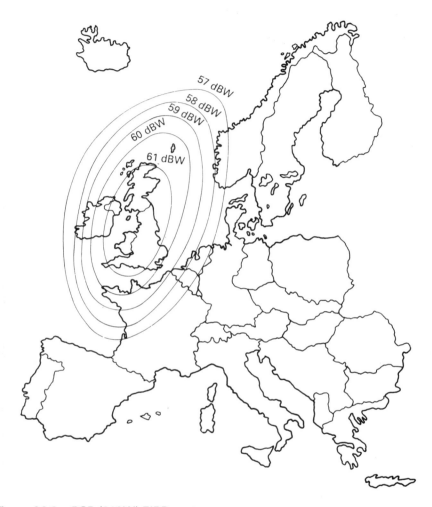

Figure A3.2   *BSB (31°W) EIRP contours*

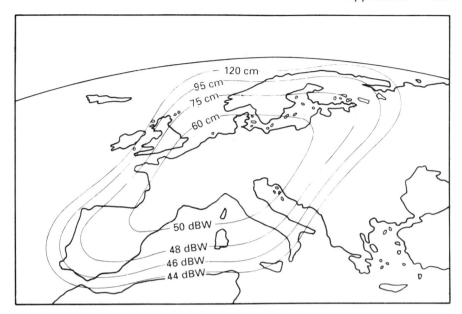

Figure A3.3 *Eutelsat II (13°E) 'Superbeam' EIRP levels (east antenna 11.6 GHz, Y polarization)*

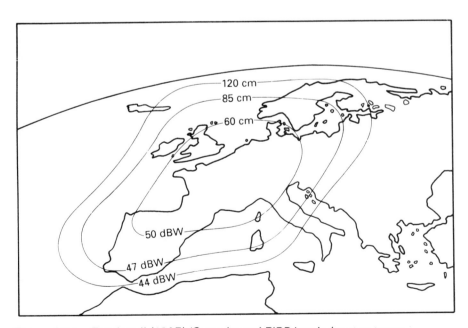

Figure A3.4 *Eutelsat II (13°E) 'Superbeam' EIRP levels (east antenna 11.6 GHz, X polarization)*

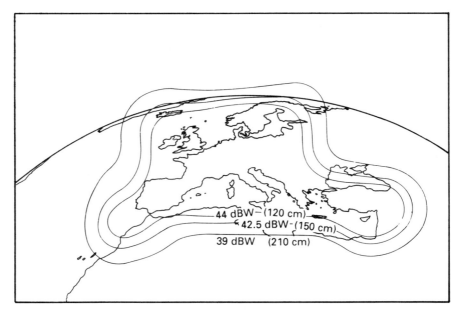

Figure A3.5 *Eutelsat II (13°E) 'Wide beam' EIRP levels (east antenna 11.6 GHz, X polarization)*

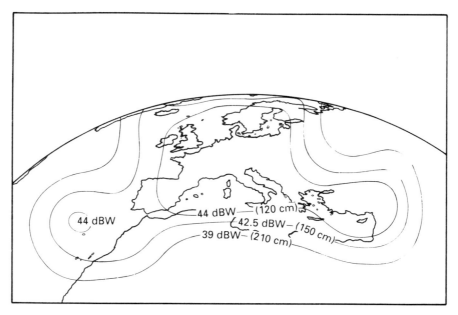

Figure A3.6 *Eutelsat II (13°E) 'Wide beam' EIRP levels (west antenna 11.6 GHz, X polarization)*

Appendix 4

Fixings (catalogue numbers for Rawlplug company products)

Table A4.1 *Rawlplug fixings*

Types and sizes
Boxes of 100 plastic plugs (in clusters of 10)

Plug colour	Ref.	Suitable screw size	Plug length mm	Drill size	Cat. no.
Green	48	Nos. 4, 6, 8 3–4 mm	20 ($^3/_4$″)	No. 8, 4.5 mm $^3/_{16}$″	**67–008**
Pink	68			No. 10, 5.5 mm $^7/_{32}$″	**67–012**
Orange	610	Nos. 6, 8, 10 3.5–5 mm	25 (1″)	No. 12, 6.5 mm $^1/_4$″	**67–016**
Grey	810			No. 10, 5.5 $^7/_{32}$″	**67–020**
White	812	Nos. 8, 10, 12, 4.5–5 mm	35 (1$^3/_8$″)	No. 12, 6.5 mm $^1/_4$″	**67–024**
Blue	1014	Nos. 10, 12, 14 5–6 mm		8 mm $^5/_{16}$″	**67–028**
Yellow	1620	Nos. 16, 18, 20	50 (2″)	11 mm $^7/_{16}$″	**67–032**

Packed in shrink wrapped outers of 10 boxes.
Source: The Rawlplug Company

Table A4.2   *Rawlbolt fixings*

Types and sizes

Ref.	Bolt size	Shield length 'A' (mm)	Fixing thickness* mm 'B' Max.	Min.	Hole dia. (mm)	Min. hole depth (mm)	Application torque for concrete (Nm)	Box qty	Cat. no.
M6 10L			10						44–015
M6 25L	M6	45	25	0	12	50	6.5	50	44–020
M6 40L			40						44–025
M8 10L			10						44–055
M8 25L	M8	50	25	0	14	55	15	50	44–060
M8 40L			40						44–065
M10 10L			10						44–105
M10 25L	M10	60	25	0	16	65	27	50	44–110
M10 50L			50						44–115
M10 75L			75						44–120
M12 10L			10						44–155
M12 25L	M12	75	25	0	20	85	50	25	44–160
M12 40L			40						44–165
M12 60L			60						44–170
M16 15L			15	0					44–205
M16 30L	M16	115	30	10	25	125	120	10	44–210
M16 60L			60	30					44–215
M20 60L	M20	130	60	25	32	140	230	10	44–255
M20 100L			100	60					44–260
M24 100L	M24	150	100	25	38	160	400	5	44–305
M24 150L			150	100					2	44–310

* *If the fixing thickness is less than the stated maximum, increase the hole depth by the difference between actual and maximum thickness.*
Source: The Rawlplug Company

Table A4.3   *Rawlok fixings*
Types and sizes
Boxes: hex nut

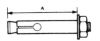

Ref. no.	Thread size	Anchor/ hole dia. (mm)	Anchor length 'A' (mm)	Min. hole depth (mm)	Max. fixture thickness (mm)	Rec. tightening torque (Nm)	Box qty	Cat. no.
R6026			26	22	5			**69–502**
R6038	M4.5	6	38		9	2.5	100	**69–504**
R6058			58	30	27			**69–506**
R8042			42		9		100	**69–508**
R8042SS								**69–308***
R8066	M6	8	66	35	35	6.0	50	**69.510**
R8092			92		60			**69–512**
R10048			48		9			**69–514**
R10048SS	M8			40		11.0	50	**69–314***
R10075		10	75		36			**69–516**
R10100			100		60		25	**69–518**
R12058			58		9			**69–520**
R12070			70		22		25	**69–522**
R12070SS	M10	12		50		22.0		**69–322***
R12098			98		50		10	**69–524**
R12126			126		80			**69–525**
R16064			64		13		20	**69–526**
R16108	M12	16	108	55	55	38.0		**69–528**
R16142			142		90		10	**69–530**
R20082			84		25		10	**69–533**
R20114	M16	20	114	60	57	95.0		**69–534**
R20158			158		100		5	**69–536**

* Indicates stainless steel Rawlok
Source: The Rawlplug Company

Table A4.4 *Rawlbor long life masonry drills*

Types and sizes STS plus shank

Dia. (mm)	Overall length (mm)	Working length (mm)	For Rawlbolt size	Cat no.
5	110	50		**28–202**
5.5	110	50		**28–206**
	160	100		**28–208**
6	110	50		**28–210**
	160	100		**28–214**
6.5	110	50		**28–218**
	160	100		**28–222**
7	160	100		**28–226**
8	110	50		**28–230**
	160	100		**28–234**
	210	150		**28–236**
10	160	100		**28–238**
	260	200		**28–242**
	450	384		**28–244**
12	160	100	M6	**28–246**
	260	200		**28–250**
	450	400		**28–251**
13	160	100		**28–252**
	260	200		**28–253**
14	160	100	M8	**28–254**
	260	200		**28–256**
15	160	100		**28–258**
	260	200		**28–260**
16	210	150	M10	**28–262**
	450	400		**28–267**
18	210	150		**28–270**
	450	400		**28–272**
20	200	150	M12	**28–274**
	450	400		**28–279**
22	250	200		**28–282**
24	250	200		**28–286**
	450	400		**28–290**
25	250	200	M16	**28–294**
	450	400		**28–296**

Source: The Rawlplug Company

Index